Môntage

Writings from a Welsh Island

Môntage
first published in Wales in 2013
on behalf of the writers by
BRIDGE BOOKS
61 Park Avenue
WREXHAM
LL12 7AW

© 2013 Môntage on behalf of the writers
© 2013 typesetting and layout Bridge Books

ISBN: 978-1-84494-089-9

A CIP entry for this book is available from the British Library

Printed and bound by
Gutenburg Press Ltd
Malta

ACKNOWLEDGEMENTS

We would like to acknowledge the support of:

- The Arts Council of Wales through the Gwanwyn Festival, organized by Age Cymru
- Phil Thomas, Director of Gwanwyn, who advised and supported our endeavour from the beginning
- Isle of Anglesey County Council
- Age Well Centres in Amlwch and Llangefni
- Medrwn Môn

We are grateful to our guest writers who generously allowed their work to be reproduced in this book

David Crystal   Tony Foster-Smith
Gwyn M Lloyd   Carol Mead
Fiona Owen   Eflyn Owen-Jones
Myrrah Stanford-Smith

Our thanks to Hilary Buckley, a local artist, who illustrated the book, Vikki Jones who designed the logo, Geoffrey Lincoln who designed the cover and David Newbould for allowing us to use one of his photographs on the cover.

We have taken advantage of the skills and kindness of family and friends who have assisted in the production of this book, in particular Angela, Muriel, Nia, Anona, and J Brandt.

CONTENTS

INTRODUCTION

The people who live on Anglesey are as varied as its landscape – wild and rugged, soft and welcoming. The island has always attracted writers, poets and artists both Welsh and English.

You have, in your hand, a unique collection of work by contemporary Anglesey writers and illustrated by a local artist. The stories and poems have been chosen by the *Môntage* editorial committee to show the variety of subject, style and talent. From memoirs to ghost stories, from historical fact to comedy, you will find something for everyone to enjoy.

As Anglesey is a bi-lingual community we have included works in both Welsh and English. The Welsh language has not been translated as we felt that it was intended to be read in the original form.

AROUND THE ISLAND IN A PIPER CUB
by Ian Hazlehurst

Standing on the tarmac at Valley Airfield I watched the Piper Cub make its final approach. A chance to see Anglesey from the air was too good to miss.

My friend, Alan, taxied the plane to a halt. 'Jump in,' he said, giving me a hand to climb aboard. 'Trip around the Island suit you?'

'Fantastic!'

We leveled out at 300ft and Alan gave me the headphones to keep in touch with the tower. 'You're in control,' he said, leaning back in his seat but watching my every move to master stability. I was a novice at powered flight but an experienced hang-glider and I quickly learned the knack.

Heading towards Rhosneigr the sky was crystal clear with no wind. We could see for miles. Rhosneigr is the wind surfing capital of North Wales but it was a quiet day.

Then we flew over the chambered cairn of Barclodiad-y-Gawres. Celts, Saxons, Romans and Vikings have all done battle for control of our strategically placed island. If you go to the local shop, you can borrow the key to explore this relic of our ancient past.

We flew on, over the Anglesey race track and soon reached Newborough Forest where red squirrels have been reintroduced. The blaze of green looked inviting.

Newborough village was literally the 'new borough' where Edward I, in 1294, relocated the population of Beaumaris to make room for his latest castle and his army.

Newborough Warren is said to be the largest area of sand in Britain.

Then we were past the sands and flying down towards the Straits with Caernarfon on our right wing. We were low enough to see the Mermaid Inn and Sea Zoo clearly on our left.

Next, we came to Brynsiencyn. The name is derived from an old story of the days when farmer Jenkins' house was the only building in this area. It is said that the house was so dilapidated it became a local landmark. The village still bears the name of its first inhabitant.

Soon we were approaching Stevenson's wonderful masterpiece, the Britannia Bridge. Alan suddenly sat up. 'Don't try and fly under it!'

Everywhere was glorious in the sunshine as we headed towards Beaumaris with its fortified castle built by Edward I to keep his wild Welsh subjects under control.

Still heading north, we turned at Puffin Island. In the 6th century the island was the home of St Seiriol and was a monastic settlement for many years. It is now uninhabited but a designated Special Protection Area because of the many seabirds that nest there. Are the puffins back? I don't know. Many were lost when a ship came aground on the island and the rats escaped. The vermin have been eliminated but whether the puffins will return in such numbers is another matter.

The sea was a sparkling, radiant blue as we crossed the wide sands of Red Wharf Bay, which stretch to the horizon, and on to the holiday resort of Benllech.

Soon we were over Moelfre, where the *Royal Charter* sank because an ambitious Captain wanted to break the record for the journey from Australia to Liverpool. Most of the passengers were returning home from years spent working in the Australian goldfields and they carried their wealth in gold bars. The weight of this gold, which they were reluctant to abandon, was the reason that many of them drowned.

Unsurprisingly, perhaps, Moelfre is a popular location with amateur divers!

On now to Dulas Island with its fierce and dangerous currents. The Lady of the Manor once discovered the bodies of castaways who had starved to death on the island and so that it should not happen again, she had a shelter built where she left food and blankets. A fireplace was made, with a chimneystack, so that she would be able to see the smoke if anyone lit a fire. She could then row across to rescue them.

We flew on to Porth Eilian, a rocky cove where you might be lucky enough to see a seal, a porpoise or even a dolphin, and turned at the Point Lynas lighthouse, towards Amlwch. People in a field waved to us and Alan reached for the joystick to waggle our wings at them.

Amlwch has played its part on the world stage. The mines of Parys Mountain were first worked in the Stone Age for flint. Later, at a time when bronze was replacing iron, the mines became famous for their copper, which was traded internationally. There are still small deposits of gold, silver and manganese left. Amlwch was once the second largest town in Wales with its own breweries and tobacco factories catering for the large population of labouring men.

From Amlwch we flew to Llanbadrig. This is the church by

the Middle Mouse rock and is said to be where St Patrick was ship-wrecked on his way to Ireland. There is fresh water and a cave nearby and the Saint lived there for several years. He built the church to give thanks for his deliverance.

Soon we were over Cemaes Bay, on the north west corner of Anglesey. It is a popular holiday resort but mostly famous because *Red Sails in the Sunset*, was written here. It is a picturesque spot. Looking back, across the Island, one can appreciate its epithet *Môn, Mam Cymru,* with its fields of green crops, animals, the occasional farmhouse, ponds and woodland, and everywhere the glorious, golden gorse drenched in brilliant sunshine.

We crossed the rocky coastline of coves and caves towards Holy Island. Then we were over Holyhead, that sprawling town with its port, mountain, quarries, famous breakwater and infamous bridge. We circled the port where ferries were waiting to sail for Ireland, and then we turned for Valley. Alan took control of the plane ready for landing.

Our journey had only taken an hour, but it was one hour in my life that I shall never forget.

AFON

gan Alan Wyn Roberts

Wrth adael y mynydd
Byrlymu mae'r nant;
Nid ydyw mor heini
I lawr yn y pant.

Ond yno mae'r dolydd
Yn donnau o rawn,
Y praidd yn lluosog,
A'r sguboriau'n llawn.

SUZIE'S DAUGHTER
by Neil Brooks

To the west of the village a footpath leads down into the valley, wide enough for vehicles as far as the cottage and outbuildings. Then it narrows to cross the fields and then the river by the slippery, planked footbridge.

A peaceful place, the old cottage, the lower walls thick, heavy stones piled in seemingly haphazard fashion. But it has stood since at least 1814 when the map first acknowledged its existence. The walls above are of a more recent date, forming a two storey home for my modern-day family.

The old barn and the stone-built sheds create two sides of the yard. Above their roofs can be seen the peaks of the mountains on the mainland and sometimes the sun will gleam off the buildings atop Mount Snowdon. The open side gives a view over the field to the wooded far bank of the river. For such a small river, the salmon in season are truly large (but whisper this quietly or we will have poachers).

Inside the cottage, the living room is the heart of the house, formed from what must have once been four rooms judging by the scars on the rough beamed, low ceiling. Here there is a fireplace with an iron oven, a trivet for the kettle and a hook to hang a pot above the flames. One winter, with the snow outside settled and frost hardened, I found a bundle of little forms huddled by the fire for warmth. Small and helpless but chests

pumping with the determination to live, lambs given to my wife by one of our farming neighbours. Too busy to spend time caring for these weak ones, they knew that she would be able to rear them to a good and successful life.

Our own dogs and cats lay just outside the group, which was a good sign. We knew from experience, that somehow the pets could tell which lambs would survive and which would not.

One lamb stood out from the others – she had a black face. She was a Blackface Suffolk, the only one amongst the group and she was to become a member of our family for many years. Normally the lambs would go back to the farm they came from but this one stayed with us and became Blackface Suzie. Or, just Suzie, for short.

Suzie was very un-sheeplike. When we appeared outside, she would come to the nearest fence and 'converse' with us. When we walked the fields to inspect the hedges and fences, she was at our heels. When we gathered our own small flock together, she would lead them to us or into their pen.

In late middle age (for a sheep), Suzie had a daughter, a Blackface, like herself. The daughter was never given her own name, she was just known as Suzie's Daughter. She didn't have her mother's intelligence, never stood out, was suspicious of the dogs – really she was just another sheep. In fact, she was more wary of us than the rest of the flock. When we needed to dose her or trim the fleece around her nether end (one of a shepherd's more messy jobs), she was more difficult to catch than the others.

Suzie grew old, as we all do, and started to lose her teeth. It is a hard fact that in nature ruminants like sheep, who have been lucky enough to survive all the other hazards of life, die of starvation. We discussed, as a family, what we should do with our Suzie. Over the years she had become part of our family but Suzie, as always, had her own way.

One day, when we drove down the lane, she was not there. Near the rocks, we saw a huddled figure and standing over it, on guard, was a Blackface Suffolk. Daughter was standing over the body of Suzie who had passed away suddenly and unexpectedly.

The following morning, at the fence to greet us, stood a familiar figure. As we walked the hedges, gathering the flock, Susie's Daughter came with us. She comes with us still. She has taken on the ways of her mother and for that, we truly love her.

Daughter's daughter, with only a trace of black around her face (for we do not know where Daughter went a-courting) runs with the flock. In time, we may find that she will one day greet us at the fence. We hope that time is far away.

MUSHROOM PICKERS

by Wendy Freeman

Fleshy texture
mingles with
earthy taste; unique.
I am transported back
to those mornings
of late summer
very early
with my father.
Me
a small girl
in shorts and wellies
on Rhosneigr common
or, as dusk fell,
beside Llyn Maelog.
He
teaching me
to pick mushrooms.

Oh, how we looked
and how we picked!
The sheep-stubbled
grass was studded
with those white pearls.

'Look underneath; look at the gills,
the fresher ones are pink,
the older ones are brown.
Smell them, Wendy,
can you smell it?
What does it smell of?'

It smells of soil
and summer,
and my mother cooking breakfast
in a cottage by the sea;
it smells of Anglesey.

AT THE PARTY
by Angela Christensen

You look at me
Enquiring eyes considering
Am I worth getting to know?

Will knowing me add something to your existence?
Have I humour, intelligence, wit?
Am I warm, nurturing and compassionate?
Do I possess knowledge of matters which might
interest you?
Am I worth your time?

You take a sip of your wine,
Ponder a moment
Then move on.

THE Z IN THE SEA
by J A Griffiths

B uilt between 1847 and 1873, Holyhead breakwater is the longest in the United Kingdom. Almost two miles in length, its peculiar Z shape has always been the subject of speculation, some people mistakenly believing that this was due to a miscalculation on the part of its designer.

Holyhead had been a small mail port for many years but a more dependable facility was deemed necessary, following the Act of Union between Britain and Ireland in 1801. There had been few passengers before then but Irish Members of Parliament were now required to attend at Westminster and a safer method by which these dignitaries could embark and disembark was considered essential. The Government ordered the building of a harbour and in 1810, work commenced on the Admiralty Pier at Salt Island to provide shelter for the natural inlet that would become the inner harbour.

Before long, the number of passengers travelling between London and Dublin had increased sevenfold and the location of a new sizable harbour in the west of mainland United Kingdom was considered. Bristol had been the main western port up to this time but it was now judged to be too far from Dublin. Liverpool suffered adverse tidal conditions, and other potential locations in North Wales were also rejected.

The building of the Menai Suspension Bridge, between 1819

and 1826, and the Britannia (rail) Bridge, between 1845 and 1850, opened the gates for Anglesey, and became the catalyst for further development to the Holyhead harbour which was a mere sixty miles from Dublin.

With the increase in shipping, a larger facility than originally planned became essential. In August 1845, James Meadows Rendel presented plans for the building of two breakwaters at Holyhead. Rendel had been trained by the respected engineer Thomas Telford and in July 1847, his plans received Government approval.

The proposal was for one of the new breakwaters to start from Soldiers Point, extend 5,360 feet in a northeasterly direction, then turn eastward towards Salt Island. The second would be built to the east of Salt Island and extend due north for 2,000 feet. This would create 267 acres of enclosed water.

Rendel was appointed Chief Engineer and George C. Dobson, Resident Engineer. The company J & C Rigby was to be the main contractor. Having acquired the necessary land, channels were marked out, railway lines were laid and a number of workshops erected on Salt Island, Newry Beach, Soldiers Point and at the base of Mynydd Twr.

At Soldiers Point, Rigby built himself a mansion styled on Hampton Court, an impressive building with turrets and battlements, which later became the Soldiers Point Hotel, before falling into disrepair. Dobson built himself a house close by, which was almost as pretentious. This building became Government House.

The nature of these buildings demonstrated the lavish lifestyles enjoyed by those in charge of the breakwater construction. It was a far cry from the living conditions of their workforce. Up to 1,300 men worked on the project at any one time. Some were recruited from far afield but most came from rural Anglesey and while some were experienced miners from Mynydd Parys, others were farmers. Many of them brought their families with them but there was little accommodation for the rapidly increasing population. Living conditions were far from adequate with no running water or sanitation. The population of Holyhead increased from 3,869 in 1841, to 8,863 by 1851.

Huge quantities of rock were blasted at nearby Mynydd Twr and transported by rail to Soldiers Point. It was then taken on to a wooden staging built into the sea before being tipped on to the seabed to create the breakwater's foundations. The 150 foot wide staging, of Quebec pine, was built to a height of 20 feet above the highest tide. Five railway lines, laid side by side, carried the rock out to sea. Blocks of dressed Anglesey limestone, quarried 20 miles away at Moelfre, were shipped by sailing boat to Salt Island, then transported by rail to form the upper part of the structure.

Blasting was a regular occurrence and the results were often unpredictable. The amount of black powder used varied between 600lbs and a massive 21,000lbs. This amount, capable of dislodging up to 130,000 tons of stone, often caused damage to houses over a mile away at Holyhead.

George Dobson designed side-tipping wagons, each able to transport 10 tones of stone from the quarry to the staging. They were moved by gravity from the rock face to the sidings below.

From there, they would be pushed by tank locomotive on to the staging and the contents tipped into the sea. The wagons were then pushed back to the quarry face, twelve at a time, using a heavy locomotive. Measured on a weighbridge, the daily load amounted to 4,000 tons. In all, a total of 7,000,000 tons of rock were used, either as a foundation or to fill the cavity between the walls.

Precarious blasting practice resulted in rock flying over a wide area and this, with the atrocious weather conditions that often faced the men on the staging, caused frequent fatalities. In the three years between 1849 and 1852, forty lives were lost. Concern was such that in 1856 Rigby, a hard taskmaster, was called before the town's magistrates who urged a greater emphasis on safety.

Even as the breakwater was being built, its value to shipping was becoming evident. One hundred and eighty-two vessels sought refuge within the harbour in 1851. By 1854, the number had increased to one thousand, eight hundred and one.

Queen Victoria and royalty from many other countries, visited the site to admire the engineering achievement. The *Great Eastern*, the world's largest ship, was diverted to Holyhead so that her passengers could view the work in progress. In fact, the vessel was forced to take refuge there for several days during the worst hurricane in living memory.

In 1854, Captain Skinner, the harbourmaster, wrote to the Admiralty expressing his view that the proposed narrow entrance to the harbour could pose difficulties for wind driven vessels. The growth in use already demonstrated that the planned 267 acres of protected water was too small for the increasingly busy harbour.

It was decided that the northern breakwater should be extended by 2,500ft in a northeasterly direction. The building of the eastern breakwater, from Salt Island, was abandoned and a harbour area of 667 acres within the extended area created. This formed the distinctive Z shape that is evident today.

James Meadows Rendel died in 1856 of natural causes. He was never to see his work completed but it is the timing of his death that has led to the story that he took his own life following an embarrassing error of judgement.

The additional 2,500ft took an extraordinarily long time to complete – almost nineteen years – but this extension, further out to sea and in deeper water, was more vulnerable to severe weather conditions. During the latter stages of construction, Rigby appeared less anxious to finish the project. He was described, at the time, as a man living comfortably with control over much government land that provided lucrative sidelines.

In 1873, following the erection of a square shaped lighthouse at its tip, the building of the 1.86 mile long structure was completed. On 19th August, twenty-six years after work began, Albert Edward, Prince of Wales, declared the work completed.

Comments were made, even then, that Rendel's original plans had been a mistake but it was certainly not an engineering miscalculation. Perhaps the word 'mistake' is misleading, though his ideas were lacking in foresight.

Captain Skinner's vision is certainly worthy of praise for it is his action that resulted in the creation of a harbour that is still capable of meeting today's needs.

The breakwater provided shelter for the creation of a pier in the late 1960s, which was used by Anglesey Aluminium. From there, undersea and underground conveyor-belts transported aluminium powder from vessels to their Penrhos Works. More recent times have seen the port develop to provide for bigger and faster ferries, travelling to and from Ireland at speeds unimaginable to those who built the breakwater.

Within the shelter of the Z in the sea, the Port of Holyhead is still developing and one cannot help but wonder what changes the next one hundred and fifty years might bring.

COELCERTH

gan Myfanwy Bennett Jones

Noson tân gwyllt ym mis Mai!
Rhubanau eirias yn cyhwfan rhwng dwylan,
Uwch y dyfnderoedd du;
Gwres y fflamau uwchben yn wynder llachar;
Nerth dur a fu'n cynnal tunelli o gyflymder
Yn cael ei ysu,
Yn toddi'n ulw.
Canrif ac ugeinmlwydd o deithio
Yn peidio
Yng nghleciadau gwreichion
Yn chwalu yng nghaddug nos.

Ni wyddem ni,
Yn nrycsawr y trannoeth,
Y codai Ffenics deublyg o ludw'r gyflafan,
A'n cysylltu eto â phedwar ban y byd.

PLAS HARVEST 1943
by Owen Charles Parry-Jones

It's July and a still morning in the field
Cae Nan'capel, and dew yet on the hay.
Across the lane is Hebron chapel, born a century
before the shadow of the road bridge
cast in concrete astride the quiet graveyard,
sun dial dealing indigo on slate,
where uncles, aunts and cousins lie
now crouched to hear the traffic,
circled by water, the slender Crigyll mill stream
snaking around the shallows
shaded by dragonfly green reeds.
Old men in flannel collar studded shirts sweating
in waistcoats at harvest time,
pitchforks planted, it's cooler to sit here in the shadow
of the sleepy blonde haycocks,
munch dark plum jam and salted butter brechdan
from the brown egg wicker basket
the scalding strong tea smelling of the hot metal
pitcher carried from Y Plas.

The strange folk are passing to the beach
in the shimmer as we wait to make hay.
For us the pleasaunce of the summer
will be a quiet hour before sunset on the sand dunes

before carrying on the morrow,
cooling our feet where the peat brown water
of Llyn Maelog spills to the flickering sea,
marram grass spears and blue butterflies gently
brush the haydust of the afternoon,
the sand trickling our effort away.
I can hear a train crossing on Tywyn Trewan,
the breeze carrying crisp lemon scents
of rabbit shorn grass from Cymyran.

As a Bryngwran schoolboy passing Bryngo
I ran down Allt Salem in schooltime for dinner in Plas,
as my father had, afraid of the *Hwch du gwta*
at the Halloween bonfires on Cae Mynydd,
neither of us aware of the ancient folk,
our ancestors who had lived there in their seasons,
and of a different DNA to the roadbuilders
who had revealed their round houses,
landscaping mine and my children's children's heritage
to their travellers' advantage.
But today we are still waiting in the shimmer
for the morning dew to pass,
to let us make hay on the morrow.

IT'S AN ILL WIND
by Mary Mason

The wrecking of the *Royal Charter*, the fastest passenger liner of her day, only a few miles from her home port of Liverpool shocked the nation. With only 40 men saved out of more than 500 passengers and crew it was one of the worst peacetime disasters in maritime history.

The *Royal Charter* was a large clipper, a three masted square-rigged sailing ship with auxiliary steam power. She was built of iron; her overall length was 32 feet.

On 26th August 1859, with a cargo of passengers and gold, the *Royal Charter* set sail from Melbourne, Australia to Liverpool, England, a journey which she had completed on the outward passage in a record sixty days. One of the passengers came from the little village of Moelfre on the north coast of Anglesey. By coincidence he was to see his home again just once before he died.

At dusk on the evening of 24th October, after a comparatively calm voyage, she was caught in the beam of the Tuskar Rock Lighthouse, off the south coast of Ireland as she rounded up and headed towards Holyhead. The weather was fine with hardly a ripple on the water and by dawn on the 25th the thin line of Bardsey Island appeared on the horizon to starboard. The light wind was in the south-east. The day was grey and bleak. By mid-day the tip of Holyhead Mountain was plain to see on the starboard bow. Although the sea was calm, there was an ominous haze over the land and an unnatural look about the sky. There was no weather forecast to tell what was coming. She plugged her way slowly northwards, her small engine beating, her long wake stretching astern and the rising wind drumming in the rigging. With her masts almost bare of canvas and with the twin bladed screw thrashing the water, she moved slowly up the coast of Anglesey, about five miles offshore.

That afternoon she came abreast of Holyhead harbour where, behind its uncompleted breakwater, reared the monstrous shape of the new great iron ship The *Great Eastern*, the biggest ship ever launched. In great excitement the passengers crowded on deck to glimpse the massive steamship designed by the engineer, I.K. Brunel. Had the master of the *Royal Charter* known what was in store, he could have put into the safe haven of Holyhead. Unknown to them all, the worst storm of the century was about to hurl its fury down the Irish Sea from the north, straight into the path of the homeward bound clipper.

Had she delayed her passage by only a day, all would have been safe and anxious relatives, waiting for the ship to dock in Liverpool, would have been able to greet their loved ones home at last from Britain's farthest flung colony. But she was the crack ship of the Australia run and her captain, Capt. Taylor, was jealous of her reputation for the fast passages on which her bookings depended. Besides which, she had weathered many gales and she was an excellent sea boat.

The hurricane struck that night, a night in which many ships were to flounder and sink. Mountainous waves built up to thwart the progress of the *Royal Charter*. She no longer responded to the wheel; she was out of control, swept before the storm like a log of driftwood, the 500 souls aboard at the mercy of any shift of the wind. No lifeboat could be launched. She was only a few miles away from Moelfre but the storm was so great that she couldn't be seen from the shore.

All over Britain it was a night of horror. On Snowdon, rocks were sent bounding down the slopes like pebbles before the screaming blast and on the rocky coast, the dull threatening boom of the breakers was continuous, with sea-spray rising 100 feet or more into the night. The *Royal Charter* tossed buoyant but helpless in the waste of foaming waves that swept her towards the savage coast which would shiver her iron hull and let in the cold ocean to snuff out all human life aboard.

The masts were cut away. The anchors were let go but at about 2.30 a.m. the last chain broke, unequal to the terrible strain. The *Royal Charter* heeled over, turned right round and drove towards the land. By comparison with the raging thunderous roar of the waves a few moments before, everything went strangely quiet as the doomed vessel wallowed in the troughs. At 3.30 a.m. she struck the rocks near Moelfre where, just around the point, there is a white shingle beach on which she would have been safe. It was low water.

Dawn broke and those on the decks stared shorewards. To their amazement they were barely 25 yards from the land. A great sea came against the broadside and divided the ship in two. People were carried down by the debris and the weight of their own clothing and drowned. The villagers, roused from sleep, ran to the cliff top and made frantic efforts to catch the ropes being thrown to the shore, but with the huge waves crashing on the rocks it was impossible to get close enough.

A passenger and a witness, James Dean, later described the scene. He saw that most of the people in the water were floundering in their heavy clothing. Some had boots on and many, unable to swim, made towards the heavier floating portions of wreckage, only to be crushed to a bloody death. In the short span twixt ship and shore, the water turned red. Seeing the terrible result of wearing too much clothing Dean took off most of his and was saved. The women, in their tight constricting stays and crinolines and the men with their wide floppy boots, found themselves in fatally unsuitable clothing. The weight of the clothing was nothing while they were in the water and buoyed up by it, but the moment of truth came when they were thrown onto the rocks and tried to stand up. They staggered under what felt like a ton weight of sodden greatcoats, trousers, waistcoats and flannel underwear. It was no coincidence that all who survived complained of being thrown ashore 'nearly naked'. It was the main factor in their survival. Another was the presence of the villagers. Of the passengers, not a woman or a child survived that terrible night.

But the title of this piece is 'an ill wind blows no good'. An ill wind it literally was. What good could possibly come from the loss of so many lives? Then, two years later, the death of the rector of Llanallgo, the church where the bodies were buried. Stephen Roose Hughes, worn out by the physical and emotional demands made on him, became ill and died in poverty. Not only had he given his heart to the bereaved but the whole of his little fortune.

However, as a direct result of this disaster and the storm of 25/26th October 1859, an inquiry was held and the British Association recommended to the Board of Trade (later the UK Met Office) that they should make use of the new electric telegraph to warn of storms in British coastal waters. In June 1860 the first official gale warnings were inaugurated.

STORM
(Hydref 26^{ain} 1859)
gan Myfanwy Bennett Jones

Brenhines y tonnau –
Ni fu ei chyflymed yn nannedd y gwynt:
Cymylau o hwyliau
A'i gyrrai ar siwrne ynghynt ac ynghynt.

Y dychweledigion
Wynebent mewn hyder ar ddiwedd eu taith,
Ag euraid ddyfodol
Yn agor o'u blaenau rôl llafur mor faith.

Ond gerllaw y glannau
Roedd bwystfil yn stelcian, yn ysu am brae,
A'i rym di-drugaredd
Yn rhuthro i rannu ei groeso o wae.

WALKING THE DOGS
by J Downs

Pebble-studded sand.
Dogs leap through pools and rushes.
Red Wharf at morning.

Dogs clear sprint over
firm, tide-cleansed, multi-toned sand.
Early at Benllech.

Foamed spray hits lighthouse.
Noisy pebble beach, wave-smashed.
Penmon at high tide.

THE TEMPEST
THE NIGHT SHAKESPEARE
CAME TO HOLYHEAD
by Myrrah Stanford Smith

It was a wild night. Hoarse ravens cawed and circled round the bell-tower – no, sorry, wrong play. We didn't present the Scottish Play until later.

This was the inaugural performance of the Ucheldre Repertory Company: *The Tempest* by William Shakespeare, to be played outdoors in the new amphitheatre. Thus far, rehearsals had been conducted in the balmy warmth of an early spring, now here we were with lowering skies and a chilly wind, listening to the weather forecast. Mike Gould, Centre manager and Duke Alonso had a hot line to RAF Valley and we hung on his words. Which way was that big raincloud coming? Would it miss us? Should we go indoors? Would anybody come?

It was the usual British gamble, madness perhaps, to add this uncertainty to the first night nerves. At least it gave us an excuse to shiver. We had a contingency plan, to play it indoors with no scenery or lighting effects. This was Shakespeare, after all. With those words what need of scenery? But we were reluctant to abandon the atmosphere and flexibility of the amphitheatre. Spirits and goddesses would line the roof, washes of coloured light would clothe the walls, the storm and shipwreck would be spectacular. Wait a little longer.

Would our audience, if any, be willing to huddle in blankets for two hours? There were those who wagged their heads and said, 'You'll never bring Shakespeare to Holyhead ...' Where was that cloud drifting now?

We reached the point of no return. The die was cast – the amphitheatre it would be. And yes, we had an audience. Wrapped in coats and rugs, they sat on small hard cushions and prepared to take what came.

Whatever the weather gods had in store, Dionysus, god of actors, smiled on us that night. The illusion was real. This was not the Anglesey School of Dance, but waves and sea-sprites and foam, the wind roared its music and the ship foundered and sank. Mrs Brackenbury's students did her proud.

Two risky pieces of casting worked. The monster Caliban was to be played by the best-looking young man in the company, but he was and is one of the best actors. He made you want to cry. Ariel was split between two players, a boy and a girl with identical colouring – auburn hair and green eyes – they were everywhere at once.

Come out now from behind the scene and, as in *Henry V*, 'let us on your imaginary forces work.' Suspend your disbelief a moment. These are no longer people you know, they are magicians and clowns, spirits and monsters, humans both good and evil; let the music of a great man's words carry you beyond make-believe into another sort of reality. You will be released soon enough. 'The cloud-capped towers, the gorgeous palaces, The solemn temples, the great globe itself, Yea, all which it shall inherit, shall dissolve, And like this insubstantial pageant faded, Leave not a wrack behind.'

This particular 'Insubstantial pageant', however, left behind some unforgettable memories. Great theatrical moments, as when Ariel cleared the banqueting table in one bare-footed leap to roar out his 'You are three men of sin,' the heart-rending scene where Caliban discovers the delights of strong drink and laughter, a Prospero who brought dignity and a sense of majesty to the part and the magic as the light faded and the wizards in the tent brought colour and life to the grey stones.

The isle was full of noises, 'sounds and sweet airs that give delight and hurt not,' the eerie alto of a young lad who spends his days busking in the streets beguiling the audience to come back after their mulled wine for the second half. We are nothing short of heroic in these islands, are we not, in the way we can ignore wind and weather? Barbecues and fetes, garden parties and open-air productions, we are game for them all. We can take our macs and boots and umbrellas and congratulate ourselves on our hardihood and if we can enjoy ourselves as well, so much the better.

The cast, the crew and evidently, the audience, did enjoy themselves. They were presenting a great masterpiece by a great master, it was exhilarating, a big thing, done to the best of their ability, against the odds. It didn't matter that the costumes were flimsy for the most part, gauzy satins and silks for the waves and spirits and goddesses. The actors were freezing but the colours were beautiful. The courtiers had the best of it in their velvets and furs, the watchers were well wrapped up, cuddled together, generating and giving out their own warmth.

I don't remember the next two performances, it was nearly

twenty years ago after all, only that the weather was kinder and the reception kinder still.

The lasting legacy in the shape of the Ucheldre Repertory Company gives thanks to that first audience, and to the Ucheldre Centre, thanks for the opportunity. To William Shakespeare all the credit.

CRABBING ON BEAUMARIS PIER

by Pauline Kenyon

Here they come in merry convoy
Rattling along the grooved decking
With their day trip paraphernalia tightly held.
Dad in the lead, clutching the newly acquired crabbing kit
Bought cheaply at the little kiosk –
Translucent bucket, filled with just enough water to become
   a trophy aquarium,
And vibrant orange crab line, complete with hook.
Whilst the youngest children carry their precious and
   mysterious bait,
Mum struggles with her knapsack of necessities –
Sandwiches, juice, wipes and other emergency kits.
At the back, snail slow and with weary, bored expressions,
Come the texting teenagers, sullenly oblivious
To the magnificence of the misty mountain views across the
   sun-sparkling water,
They wish themselves elsewhere –
Anywhere where their sophisticated juvenility would be at home.

Dad demonstrates the finer points of setting bait,
Shaking off eager little helping hands that might endanger
   his tutorial,

Then every eye watches the twisty descent
As he carefully lowers the line into the water.
Small heads poke through the railings to get a better view
Tingling with impatient excitement.
The line jerks erratically making a whirlpool in the sea
And Dad can scarcely contain his pride as he retrieves the line
And a clinging crab appears, reluctant to loosen its tenacious grip.
Squeals of delight startle the teenagers from their messaging
As their younger siblings urge on their outwardly fearless father
In his nervous efforts to avoid the nipping claws and pop the
    hapless crab into the bucket.
Everyone stands in awe of the handsome catch and all become
    children again.
A severe and contagious rash of broad smiles breaks out!

Suddenly the competition begins ...
Teenagers stow their phones away in back pockets and advance
To offer their superiority to the little ones.
The lines haul up and down, the foolish crabs are caught,
The others wriggle free and plop back into the lapping waves –
Some to be caught again almost immediately –
And the bucket fills with assorted victims.
Mums hover with sandwiches and worry about wet and
    grimy hands.
Dads are sent for ice-creams – and more bait.
Teenagers and little ones count the catch and work together,

Sharing skills, laughter and teasing chases with the latest crab
thrashing in the victor's hands
Keeping fingers safely out of the way of determined, clashing
claws!
Hours pass in total absorption and simple, joyous activity on the
pier head.
The unfathomable wonder of crabbing on the pier
Has worked its unifying magic yet again.

PREDICTION
by Kay Middlemiss

In the dark hour before dawn the man rode out from Penmynydd, turning east towards the Straits and the mainland. Although he was a nobleman his entourage was small. He took enough men to protect him and his precious charge – a long and dangerous journey lay ahead – but he wished to travel anonymously. A Welshman on his way to London to seek his fortune. Nothing more. Maredudd ap Tewdwr could not have foreseen that the boy who rode beside him would one day change the history of England and Wales for all time.

The sound of their jingling harnesses carried far over the still marshes and Margaret ferch Dafydd, standing in the doorway of the small manor house that was their family home, listened and wondered when, or if ever, she would see her husband and son again.

The riders followed the track over land that had once belonged to Maredudd but was now forfeit to the English King. The fortunes of war had turned against the Tewdwrs when Owain Glyndŵr's rebellion had failed. Maredudd had supported Glyndŵr, he was his cousin, but now he had to look to his own future and that of his son Owain.

At the Straits the riders turned north towards the crossing place. The diminishing waves surging through the narrow sea-passage told Maredudd he had timed the tide exactly. If they were not at the crossing place by low tide they would have to wait another day before they could make an attempt to reach the mainland. He would not risk his men and horses by crossing the sandbar at night.

It was full daylight by the time they reached the headland. A group of people were standing on the shore and Maredudd saw immediately that something was wrong. From the opposite bank a farmer was trying to herd his cattle across to the Island but, too impatient, he had started too soon. Halfway across the tide was still running high and the cattle were out of their depth. Instinctively they began to swim but with no one to guide them they had no sense of direction. Some were carried out to sea while others were caught by the treacherous rocks in midstream. The herdsmen, in their heavy clothing, could not swim out to reach them. Those beasts that did make it to the shore were caught by the waiting villagers.

'He'll not see them again,' laughed the soldiers but Maredudd was angry.

'Get your cattle out of the way!' he shouted. 'You're blocking our path.' But the men could not control the panicking animals. All Maredudd could do was to watch as the brief interval of safety ebbed away and the waters began to rise once more.

'A bad beginning,' he said to his son.

'An omen,' the soldiers began to mutter.

An experienced soldier himself, Maredudd knew that if he turned back for home his men would not be willing to set out again the following day. 'We go on,' he told them. 'Tonight we will stay at Penmon Priory.' They were not local men, they would not question his decision.

Over dinner that night Maredudd entertained the good brothers of Penmon Priory, recounting the events at the cattle crossing. As he was explaining how he had deceived his men into thinking there was another route to the mainland he noticed a woman standing in the doorway.

She was old and bent, dressed in rags and her long hair was matted and filthy. For no reason he could name Maredudd shivered as her sharp glance met his, then came to rest on the boy, Owain, his son.

'Who is that old crone?' he asked the brothers. 'She looks like a witch. What is she doing in the Priory?'

'She is a wise-woman,' one told him. 'She is a hermit and lives by the Holy Well. You are lucky she has come here tonight for she has 'the sight' and can tell the future.'

'You are going on a journey,' said another. 'It can be helpful for a traveller to know that he will arrive safely at his destination. Shall we bring her over to you?'

Maredudd sighed. As a soldier he believed that sometimes it is better not to know the outcome but a brother was already leading her between the long tables. With a shock Maredudd saw that she was blind. He was sure she had looked at him and at the boy.

The woman bowed her head to Maredudd as he searched for some coins and threw them onto the table in front of her. The woman ignored them. She ignored Maredudd. She turned her sightless eyes towards Owain.

'You are going to London?' They had not told anyone this was their destination but it would not have been a difficult guess.

'You will live in luxury there. In a Royal Palace.' Maredudd could see the excitement in his son's face.

'Yes. My kinsman, Lord Rhys, has arranged for me to be a page in the Steward's household but most of all I want to be a soldier and fight in France.' Owain was too young to know that it is better not to tell your future plans to a fortuneteller.

'Owain!' his father warned.

'How old are you Owain?'

'Seven years, lady.'

'Too young to achieve your dreams just yet but you will ... and much, much more. Give me your hand, child.'

Maredudd shuddered as his son placed his soft, childish hand in the filthy claw of the seer. It was as if lightening passed between them. Candles flickered and the brothers fell silent. The blind woman placed her other hand on Owain's head.

'Black curls,' she said. 'On a head that will one day rest in the lap of a queen.' She dropped to one knee, touched the toe of the boy's riding boot and was gone from the room.

Maredudd gathered up the coins and gave them to the brothers for the old woman's food. He was puzzled, and a little worried if he was honest, about the mention of a queen's lap. His son was gently bred and already a handsome lad. He hoped it wasn't a warning of future trouble.

But Owain had no thoughts beyond his immediate dream. 'I am going to be a soldier. Did you hear, Father? And I shall fight in France. I suppose it will be all right to learn to be a courtier first though.'

The hermit went back to her cave at the Holy Well amazed by

all that had been revealed to her that night. She had only told a small portion – it was not good for a child to know everything. The queen she had seen in her vision was a young French princess. She had been given the name Catherine but how a union with the Welshman could come about she did not know. Of one thing though, she was certain, from the line of Tewdwr – or Tudor as it would be known – would come two of the greatest monarchs the land would ever see.

OWL TIME
by Rosalind Pulvertaft

Is it still owl time
Out there in the graveyard?
Squat silhouettes
In swaying ash branches.

Then all of an instant
Fled with the night time
Only chill winds of Winter
Now stir those bare branches.

Can mice now creep safely
Amid the rank grasses?
'Til slinking from firesides
Cats hunch on the tombstones.

SUNDAYS
by E Pritchard

I've never been very keen on Sundays. I think it goes back to my Holyhead childhood of having to attend chapel three times a day. We had special Sunday clothes to wear on that day and that day only. I didn't like going to chapel or having to learn a verse from the Bible to recite in front of the whole congre-gation which, in those days, was a large one.

The only good thing about Sundays was the roast dinner at lunchtime. My parents had their routine: the vegetables were prepared on Saturday and stood in the scullery in bowls of cold water; the dried peas were put to soak with their tablet of bicarbonate of soda. My mother would par-boil the potatoes before we left for chapel so that they could be roasted when she arrived back home – about an hour before us. The meat was put on low in the oven.

The children stayed in chapel for half the morning service and then we filed out to a room upstairs where we had to attend another service. In order to get out of going to the children's service I sometimes used to turn to my mother and whisper 'Did you remember to switch the potatoes off?' She would give me a hard stare, but I had obviously sowed the seed of doubt in her mind as she would quietly pass me the house key and I would then dash off home instead of going upstairs with the other children. What bliss to be stepping home to an empty house.

The potatoes were off of course, but in gratitude of my escape I would set the table. I couldn't try this trick very often - most of the time she was positive that she had turned the potatoes off!

After lunch we children had to wash up. Washing up after a roast dinner was never fun even though we had enjoyed the meal. There was a piece of soap in a metal cage with a handle that we shook in a bowl of very hot water but even so, those burnt bits in the corners of the roast potato tin were a devil to remove.

Then it was Sunday school. We were split up into classes according to our ages and we had to learn a verse from the Bible, usually several. At the end it was announced which class had learned the most verses. It was a very long hour. Back home then, and straight home too – there was no going out to play on a Sunday. Good gracious no! We were allowed to read and also to knit and sew. This was probably because my mother liked to do so but, whenever her mother called to see us, all knitting and sewing had to be put away in case our grandmother saw it. We were allowed to play some games but never cards which would have been sinful. I used to look through the window and see my friends out playing but they all knew better than to call and ask me to join them. When my parents were young they weren't allowed to run on a Sunday even if they were late for chapel.

Soon it was time for tea. The table was set with a nicely embroidered tablecloth and a china tea set, napkins neatly rolled in their napkin rings. There would be a plateful of bread and butter and some jam. I didn't like it when the jam was my grandmother's rhubarb variety or Aunty Katy's gooseberry jam.

Sometimes it was a piece of cheese or, even better, my father would have opened a tin of salmon – John West Red Salmon, no less. If we didn't eat our bread and butter we weren't allowed to have what came next. My mother was a good cook and her sponge cakes were always well risen but she was mean with her finishing touches. Her Victoria sponge had such a thin layer of jam and her fairy cakes were spread with such a thin layer of watery icing and sliver of glacé cherry that they seemed dry. How I used to love it when she had no time to bake and we had SHOP CAKE! My favourites were Kunzle cakes. I loved them. It was my ambition to have a whole box to myself. Sadly, by the time I grew up they were no longer available. After we had eaten our cake the final course was jelly and fruit. How we hoped that it was strawberry jelly (not the green one) and fruit cocktail. We used to have to take turns as to who was to have the cherry as they seemed to put only one in each tin. I don't like cherries even to this day but if it was my turn to have the cherry, by golly I was going to have it. With this we would have either tinned cream, which had to be shaken as it would have separated in the tin, or evaporated milk. I was never keen on the cream as it seemed to dry my teeth but in those days children didn't say they didn't like things – they just ate what was put in front of them. When we had orange jelly and tinned mandarins the evaporated milk would curdle in the juice.

After clearing the tea dishes it was time for chapel again. The family's seat was upstairs in the gallery. I spent my time counting the number of organ pipes as if they would have changed from week to week, or counting the number of deacons in the 'sêt *fawr'*. I enjoyed the hymn singing but that was all. Sometimes we would have a triangular paper bag with mint imperials, known as *'candies capel'*. Woe betide us if we allowed the bag to split and the sweets to fall as they would bounce around noisily and seemed to echo round the whole chapel. Towards the end of the service it was time for the children to make their way to the front to say yet another verse. My journey was longer than most, being up in the gallery, and by the time I arrived they had started, taking each child in turn and listening to their verses. This meant I was usually last. I am not, and never have been, any good at quoting verbatim any verse, poem or quotation no matter how I like them, so remembering my verse was always difficult for me. Many a time I had to resort to a short old favourite like *'Duw, cariad yw'*. This never went down well with my parents!

Back home again for a bath, some cereal for supper, and bed. Thank goodness, another Sunday over.

SUL YM MIL WYTH TRI DAU

gan Myfanwy Bennett Jones

'Roedd John Jones o Lanfair yn deiliwr o fri,
A'i grefft oedd yn destun edmygedd
Ymhell ac yn agos, gan fonedd a gwreng,
A'r galw am ei waith yn ddiddiwedd.

Un Sul, 'roedd yn hwylio i gychwyn ar daith
Yn fore, yn ôl ei arferiad,
A'i fryd ar dramwyo saith milltir a mwy
I gapel ym Mhentraeth, yn gennad,

Pan glywodd ei wraig yn y gegin islaw
Yn brysur ymddiddan â rhywun.
Pwy allai fod yno mor fore â hyn
Ac am ba beth 'roedd yn ymofyn?

Prysurodd i wisgo a disgyn o'r llofft
Er mwyn gweld pwy oedd yr ymwelydd,
Ac yno'n llawn ffwdan, â'i wynt yn ei ddwrn,
Pwy welai ond stiward Plas Newydd.

'John Jones,' meddai 'rhaid ichi ddyfod ar frys.
Mae'ch angen ar deulu y Plasdy.
Bydd gofyn cyflawni swyddogaeth o bwys!
Wel, brysiwch! Dowch, – heddiw, nid 'fory!'

'Pa fath o swyddogaeth, ar fore dydd Sul,
A mi ar fin mynd i bregethu?
Mi fyddaf yn deiliwr yfory, 'run fath.
A dof i Blas Newydd bryd hynny.'

Ar hyn fe ostyngodd y stiward ei lais:
'Mae hyn yn beth gwir gyfrinachol.
Mae dwy dywysoges yn aros 'n y Plas,
Ar saib o'u gorchwylion brenhinol.

'Mae'r ferch, – sef Victoria, – un fach fywiog iawn,
Ar geffyl yn fawr ei medrusrwydd.
Mae'n treulio cryn amser hyd erwau y Plas
Ar garlam, waeth beth fyddo'r tywydd.

'Ond ddoe cafodd ddamwain, – fe rwygodd ei gwisg
Ac nid oes 'run arall yn gweddu
I eneth mor fechan. Ac felly mae brys
Am grefftwr fel chi all ei helpu.'

Ond meddai y teiliwr yn gadarn ei lais,
'Bydd raid iddi aros tan fory.
Mi fyddaf yn barod ben bore i'r gwaith,
Ond heddiw 'rwy'n mynd i bregethu.'

'Ond ddyn!' gwaeddai'r stiward, a'i wyneb yn fflam,
'Mae hwn yn orchymyn brenhinol!
Ni allwch er dim anwybyddu'r fath wŷs.
Mae hynny yn dramgwydd difrifol!'

'Mi gefais orchymyn brenhinol cyn hyn,'
Oedd geiriau di-amod y teiliwr.
'A mynd 'nôl fy arfer Sabothol a wnaf,
Yn ufudd, i fod yn bregethwr.

'Nid ydwyf ond teiliwr fan yma, mae'n wir,
Yn gweithio i werin a bonedd,
Ond yn y byd nesaf, wrth orsedd y Tad,
Gobeithiaf gael lle o anrhydedd.'

Pan glywodd 'r ymwelwyr ymateb fel hyn
Yr oeddent yn wir yn rhyfeddu
At safiad mor gadarn a dewr gan y gŵr,
Ac ni allent lai na'i edmygu.

A thrannoeth pan aeth tua'r Plas at ei waith
Fe roddwyd i'r teiliwr orchymyn, –
Pe cawsai ei hun mewn anghaffael ryw dro
I fynd yn ddi-feth ar eu gofyn.

Ond chafodd Victoria 'run cais gan John Jones
A dreuliodd ei fywyd mewn urddas
Yn fawr ei ymlyniad i Frenin sydd fwy,
Yn ffyddiog o'i le yn ei Deyrnas.

SHEARWATER
by Marjorie Humphreys

Darkness descends and the day turns grey,
There is movement in the burrows where they will not stay,
Instinctively knowing when the time is right
To prepare for their adventure and solitary flight.
The moon begins to rise and throws long ghostly shadows
On the sea and the trees and the grassy hollows,
Soft cooing is heard and an almost silent flutter,
And then, silhouetted wings on the wall appear.
Glimpses of minute white faces staring at the stars,
Practice without words how to navigate afar,
Calmly trusting their knowledge that comes from within,
How to map out the world and where to begin.
Then one launches off out towards their freedom search,
And under the shadow of the wings I almost lurch,
With wonder and amazement at the power of creation,
And I gaze once more at the stark faces, on the wall of
proclamation.

(I wrote this poem after having the privilege of watching some young Shearwaters fly from their nests for the first time on Ynys Môn.)

A BRIEF ENCOUNTER
by Elaine Powell

For two whole days Ted Jones and his 12 year old son Joe have been forced to stay in their caravan due to torrential rain. They had made plans to walk the coastal path of Anglesey as part of their holiday. So when the weather begins to improve they put on their waterproof clothing and head out to the lighthouse at Point Lynas. They set off westwards towards Amlwch Port. The ground beneath their boots is sticky with the rain and they walk with care, keeping their eyes on the stony earth and the cliff edge. The sea on their right is gently nudging the rocks on the shore below. Suddenly Joe stoops down and picks something up.

'Look Dad – treasure!' he says excitedly and shows his father the muddy coin in his hand.

'Let me have a look – Hmmm I think it's an old penny – there used to be 240 of them in a pound. Your grandparents would remember them. Let me see what the date is.' Ted wipes it on his jeans and holds it up in the sun. 'My goodness, this isn't an old penny – it's a large halfpenny but not one that I've ever seen before. It's dated 1788 and look at the words around the edge – they say 'Payable in Anglesey, London or Liverpool'. On one side it says 'The Anglesey Mines' and on the reverse side there's the head of an old man with a long beard wearing a hooded cloak. Can you see the design of leaves all around the edge? Well

I never – I'll put it safely in my zipped pocket and we can look it up on the internet when we get back.'

More than two hundred years before, on the same piece of ground, a woman had stood looking out to sea. Her black skirt reached just above her wooden clogs and a brown woollen shawl was wrapped around her head and shoulders. Thick black curls framed her handsome face.

She was watching the sailing ships and was thankful that it was a fine day with just a light breeze. Her thoughts were with one particular ship called the *Sandwich*. It was bound for Liverpool. It would be a long journey if the wind remained light. However she knew that the wind and sea conditions could change very quickly. She had seen waves so high that only the tops of the sails were visible when the ships sank low in the valleys of the swell. And she had heard the roar of the ocean so loud that it drowned out the distant sounds of the explosions in the mines at Mynydd Trysclwyn.

She began to muse about a time before the prospectors arrived here to explore Parys Mountain and to sink those first shafts deep down into the earth. Her ancestors had told many stories about how the ancient copper mines had been worked by the Romans hundreds of years ago. The golden lagoon had been there for as long as anyone could remember and her own father used the orange waters to cure the foot rot in his sheep. She was just a child when the mines had been re-opened and she remembered the excitement in the town when the road, from Parys Mountain all the way down to the port, was completed. There had been so much work for local men.

She was roused out of her reveries by a strange voice. 'Good day to you. Augustin Lentin, ma'am.' She turned and saw a tall gentleman dressed in a long fine overcoat. He had doffed his hat to her. She smiled as she recognised him. She had seen him around the town and at the copper mines but she had never spoken to him. She returned his greeting and introduced herself as Mistress Sydney Jones.

When the mines had started working again there had been an influx of newcomers to the town, mostly from England but also men from much further afield. The great open cast mine was of great interest to many people. She even recalled the day a famous scientist called Michael Faraday had visited the area. She hadn't been able to understand the way any of them spoke and yet this foreign gentleman was now speaking to her in her mother tongue.

'It's a calm sea today,' he said. 'Have you menfolk on those ships?'

'Yes,' she replied. 'It's my son Edward's first time on board – he's only 12 years old. The men were loading the copper ore much earlier this morning, along with fresh goods and livestock from the local farms. It'll be a few days before he returns.'

'I'm sure you're happy there's fair weather. I suppose you have seen a lot of changes here?' he said.

She nodded her head. 'I certainly have. Not many years ago it was very quiet. My father farmed these fields before the mines were opened and we lived in a long stone dwelling which he built with the help of his brothers. The reeds of the thatched roof could barely withstand the winter storms, despite being strengthened in the autumn. It's a miracle that any of us managed to survive the damp and the cold. When we were small we played on the shore and collected shellfish and pocket crabs for supper. There were just a few families living here then but now in the town there are streets of sturdy stone houses all joined together. They have an upstairs groglofft for the bedroom and a back yard with a *tŷ bach*. There are hundreds of people living here and many have come here from England. There's plenty of work for everyone and even my father has a job at the mines. But I hate the sulphurous smog and tainted atmosphere that blankets the town on most days. You'll notice the coughing I expect?'

'Yes I've have heard it a lot. It's hard now to imagine how peaceful it must have been. Everything is noisy and dusty with the constant activity in the mines but as you have just said, it's brought lots of work for everyone and great wealth for some. I have come here to study the way the copper is extracted and smelted. In Germany, where I live, we use a different method and it's not so efficient.'

'You speak our language' she said smiling.

'Yes. I have plenty of time to study in the evenings,' he said,

'I've seen you working with the other women haven't I? What is it you actually do?'

'We're called the 'copper ladies,' she said. 'You will have seen us sitting outside the Charlotte yard using our heavy hammers to chip away at the great lumps of ore that are brought to the surface of the mine. These lumps encase the precious copper and it's our job to pound away without spoiling it. We hold the lumps with our left hands on a rectangular iron block we call the knockstone and wield the hammer with our right hands. We try to chip off fist-sized pieces. Some chunks are a mix of lead and copper and others have pure copper inside. We have to sort these into separate heaps. It's tough work and very long hours and by the end of the day I'm exhausted. I get a lot of pain in my knees because we have to kneel whilst we work. Have you noticed the gauntlet that we wear on our left hands? They are made of strong leather. Rings of iron circle the fingers and thumb to protect us from the heavy blows of the hammer. We have to buy them from the company shop and they cost a day's pay. We also have to buy the hammers.'

'I've noticed that you have your own currency here. You get paid with tokens and I guess the shop only takes the tokens?'

'Yes that's right and we have to pay its high prices. We can also spend them in the markets and my son says that he will be able to spend them in Liverpool.'

Herr Lentin delved into his waistcoat pocket and pulled out a handful of coins. He held them out in his palm and looked at them carefully. 'Who is the person with the cloak around him?' he asked.

'He's a Druid priest. Druids were the ancient people who lived on this land before the time of the Christian saints. Many years ago this island was a stronghold for the Druids.'

All of a sudden a group of youths rushed past and accidentally bumped into *Herr* Lentin. The coins fell to the ground. The boys were most apologetic and gathered them up in haste and returned them to their owner. No-one noticed that one coin lay on the ground in the shadow of a stone.

References

Copper Kingdom, Amlwch Industrial Heritage Trust.

Parys Mountain and the Lentin Letters, translated by Nancy Rothwell.

Copper Mountain, John Rowlands.

The Copper King, J R Harris, Anglesey Archives.

NATUR AR FYNYDD PARYS

gan Gwyn M Lloyd

Un diwrnod tyfodd blodyn – herfeiddiol
O ganol pob gwenwyn,
Baw a rhwd yn bur o wyn.
Mor hudol grym yr hedyn.

THE SAILOR'S RETURN
(By Train from Chester)
by Neil Brooks

I sat by the window, longing to be
Home again in Llanfair PG.
But then the train pulled into Flint
And the chap beside me coughed a hint,
Removed his glasses, mopped his brow
And persisted in relating how
He always caught this train these days –
And breathed on me a whisky haze –
And would I join him in a drink?
(I'd already heard his carrier clink)
And this train it was so very good,
And – Oh, wouldn't I? But he would, he would;
And he didn't used to drink you know
And on he went relating how
He'd had a breakdown at his work,
'Cause he'd work too hard, and never shirk
From adding columns morn 'til night
But his nervous breakdown was a fright,
And he'd had to go into a place
And learn once more the world to face,
And his wife was good, and saw him twice
In every week, and the place was nice.
And when, in time, they thought him well

They'd sent him home and – and – Oh hell!
(He poured some more and swallowed it,
And then recovered, bit by bit.)
So, when he got home, his wife-of-years
Was weeping, sobbing, crying tears,
And put him on a sofa-bed,
Because, you see, his old friend, Ted,
Was living, living there where he
Should and would and ought to be.
And in the end he'd packed and gone,
And now he lived so all alone,
And – What did I do? Oh, you're at sea?
Now that would have been the job for me.
Never to have balanced page on page
And faced the M.D.'s nasty rage,
And – now he hadn't worked for years –
Again I saw a hint of tears –
Then 'Penmaenmawr' came the porter's shout,
And he grabbed his bag, and hurried out.
Two stops more and I would be
Back home again in Llanfair PG.

ONE LAST TIME
by J Downs

Baz Mitchell was twenty-three years old and he was going to start being honest. He'd had enough of cells and prison food. He was definitely going to be honest after this. He just needed some quick easy cash to set him up.

'It's simple man,' Daf, his cell mate, had said and then had told him exactly where on Anglesey the tiny general store and post office was. It didn't even have security cameras. 'It's open Tuesday and Thursday afternoons. Tuesday's best because Thursdays the old farts get their pensions. Go next Tuesday before the kids break up on Friday. It's more crowded at holiday time. It'll only take you a couple of hours on your bike from Manchester. I'll draw you a map.'

Daf had been good to him. Stood up for him and that. Didn't even hold it against him when Baz had been forced to grass on him. What else could he do when the weed hidden in the cell, had come to light? 'Happens to the best of us,' Daf said, 'Bloody screws have all the clout.'

Baz remembered what Daf had said to him two days ago as the huge gates of Strangeways had clanged behind them. 'Surprise boy – that's the secret. Go in looking innocent, stand just inside the door and whip out the gun. Like I said, a toy one – they can look just like the real thing. The old trout'll throw the money at you. No sweat.'

It had all gone right so far. Bought a dead ringer for a gun at a pound shop. Lovely weather this morning for a ride on the Honda. On the coast road, blue sky and blue sea with those white bits on top of the waves. When he passed Colwyn Bay, he'd remembered having a day out there, with his Nan, years ago. No queue over the bridge. Easy to find the village. Daf was good at maps. No-one about on the street. He parked the bike outside the post office for a quick get-away.

No customers inside the dim shop which smelt of biscuits and candles. The old trout, a small, white-haired woman is shoving notes, from the till, into a plastic bag. He'll be out of here in a minute, on the bike and away. No problem. Baz stands up tall. He's the clever one. He'll tell Daf all about it – Daf, always the boss, who thinks himself better than …

Crash! Baz is thrown forward as the door's flung open into his back. The toy gun shoots from his grasp and clatters on to the stone floor.

'Stay cool.' He can hear Daf's voice inside his head. 'Never panic.' But panic is already in his throat. He can feel it in the thumping of his heart and the pounding inside his head as he feels blindly on the dark floor for the gun, first with his right hand then with his left.

Baz screams as something crushes his groping hand. The pain is unbelievable. He can just see a small black boot, pinning it to the ground. He can't move it. Then he sees the face of the old woman down, at his eye level and she's smiling. Something presses hard into the side of his head. He hears a click at the same time as he sees his toy gun on the floor, a couple of feet away. In horror he realises that a real one is at his head and that the safety catch is off.

The old bitch grinds her foot into his hand and Baz thinks he hears himself screech as he topples to the ground, but he isn't sure. Then he hears a man's laugh, strangely familiar, right behind him. 'Are you all right, Nain? What a star! You didn't need me after all. Now wipe the gun and press his right hand to it.' Agony engulfs Baz as the bitch gives his hand a final mashing with her boot. The voice continues, 'I'll put it where the cocky little grass dropped his toy, right? Now you dial 999.'

Baz forces himself to look behind at the speaker. Then the pain and the shock overcome him and he passes out at the feet of his mentor, Daf Jones.

PADDLING IN WELLIES
by Pauline Kenyon

In the winter when the sun is low and watery weak,
And the Anglesey wind can cut through the warmest
  clothes,
We love to go to the beach at Benllech.
We stride across the oozing sand following the crazy,
  drunken bird tracks
And the deep and wondrous claw marks left by joyous,
  galloping dogs
And go paddling in our wellies!

Oh, the sheer delight of walking in the waves
Feeling the chill of swirling water round our safely
  snug feet,
Watching the surging whirlpools round our rubber booted
  ankles!
We plough up and down and risk a splash or two,
Or even some timid wave jumping in the shallows,
Stomping around in a wintery paradise –
And no itchy sand between our cosy toes.

Then we see just how far into the depths we can recklessly
  venture
With the cold sea creeping dangerously up our welly
  boot sides

Like a stormy ocean beating against a sturdy
   lighthouse,
Before a wayward, misjudged wave slops a freezing
   douche over the rim
And leaves us gasping in hilarious horror at the icy
   drenching.
Then briskly we go clomping back to the car to
   change into our shoes –
And laugh all the way home.

THE LADY IN WHITE
by Katherine Hutchings

I saw her again, last night – the lady in white. I may have been dreaming or it may have been on one of my night-time wanderings through the empty chapel. When you reach my age the thin line between dreams and reality can become a little blurred. But she was there. I always know when she is there.

'What are you doing in the chapel in the middle of the night?' you are asking.

Well, it's part of my home, you see. I live in that little bit that's built on to the chapel, at the back. My husband was the caretaker and I did the cleaning and looked after things.

After my husband died they allowed me to stay on in the house. By this time the congregation had dwindled to a handful and no minister could be found so they decided to close our chapel. The pews and furnishings were sold and the windows boarded up but I still keep it tidy. I have the key and I only have to walk through a door from my kitchen.

'But in the middle of the night?' you are thinking.

Yes. Since I moved my bed downstairs, because of the leaking roof, I often get up in the night to make a pot of tea. There is something peaceful about the chapel at night. I light the oil lamp and the boarded windows and empty corners hide in the shadows. I remember a time when the singing of the congregation could be heard through the whole village. Those times will never come again.

But the lady in white will come. She stands at the place where the pulpit used to be. She wears a long white gown and her hair is hidden beneath a soft veil or shroud. I know she is not real. She is like a picture projected onto the chapel's stone but there are no hidden cameras here. She has her back to me and I know that she is quietly weeping. I long to talk to her, to comfort her, this stranger, but as I move towards her she vanishes into thin air – my lady in white.

There is great excitement in the village. There is to be a wedding and it seems that almost everyone has become involved. It's my granddaughter, you see. Although she left Anglesey when she was only a babe she wants to get married in the village where she was born. There will be a lot of guests and people are staying in the houses of friends of friends and so on. I couldn't put anyone up because of the leak.

I said she should get married in the chapel – generations of our family have been married there. But she said: 'Don't be silly, Nain. The chapel is almost derelict. The wedding will be at the hotel, they've got a licence and they'll organize the reception afterwards. All you have to do is buy yourself a new outfit and be the guest of honour.'

On the morning of the wedding I am woken early by the insistent ringing of the doorbell. I am amazed to see my granddaughter standing on the step with a young man I do not recognize – it's certainly not her fiancé – and they are both carrying cases.

'Good gracious! You're not eloping?'

My granddaughter laughs and introduces the young man as her wedding photographer.

'You know, Nain, I've been thinking about what you said – about our family all getting married in the chapel. It's too late to change anything but I thought it would be nice to have a photograph taken there. Even if it isn't the real wedding...' She stops, embarrassed, and I can tell that this is important to her.

'Yes, of course, but you'll have to hurry.' I hustle her into my bedroom then show the photographer into the chapel. 'Now, you get everything ready while I put the kettle on.'

I don't know what I expected to see when I walked back quietly into the chapel, but what I saw I shall never forget. There she stood – my lady in white.

Was I dreaming as I walked towards her? I held out my arms and this time she did not vanish. She turned toward me, throwing back her bridal veil and I saw that her tears were of joy, not sorrow.

'Oh, Nain, this is the most wonderful day of my life.' We held each other very close. 'Will I always be this happy?'

'Not always, child. Happiness is very precious, enjoy it while you are young. Sorrow is for the old.'

I have that photograph beside my bed. I often look at it and wonder if my lady in white was a ghost or a premonition. If I was seeing into the future that means our choices have already been made and I don't like the idea of predestination. On the other hand, a record of the past must signify history repeating itself. Is life one great circle continuously being re-enacted? These mysteries are too deep for me to understand. But I am an old woman and it won't be too long now before these questions are answered for me.

BAI AR GAM

gan Gwyn M Lloyd

Ni haeddaf fy nghyhuddo – o'r drosedd
O gloi'r drws ar Seilo;
Camwedd oedd ei ddiwedd o
Mi wn – ond do'n 'im yno.

SIWAN'S FAREWELL
by Owen Charles Parry-Jones

To chance and the Prince's quiet satisfaction
that February the weather was mild
for the short journey.
Siwan
would not be waving
her fair hand and arm raised in salute,
her oxter angle open
allowing a falling mantle
to reveal her bare defiant shoulder.
Llanfaes beckoned
The Royal Barge,
the Ferryman having had more than his usual fourpence,
slid from Abergwyngregyn over Lafan
as the head of the Orme abaft
gnawed the line of the horizon,
margin even of yesterday's dominion.
The ebb lapped,
today her realm suddenly expanded
as she left Llywelyn Fawr
her primum mobile
and his conquered boundaries,
for her empyrean,
fulmars wheeled above

with their exaggerated dihedral.
Y Tywysoges Siwan,
Princess Joan, moved slowly further
to an outer sphere,
from the flat shore,
from William Brewys unmanacled *en fin*
buried in the hillside bracken.
She could see it all now mid-stream,
the fat round Tower and the Gatehouse
the hills, the Falls behind
sheltering Garth Celyn,
in the Hafod the cattle at milking,
the Gardens and home.
Joan would lie for seven centuries
on the island
under the floral carved stone,
in the Friary and then wilderness.
The priests meet her
as they will for her grandson's wife
Eleanor de Montfort
dying in childbirth of Gwenllian.
Bare voices chant
intermittent halfnotes
to greet her,
Siwan
wife, mother and daughter of Princes.

TRAGEDY ON THE NARROW WATERS
by Elaine Powell

Hugh opened the back door to check on the weather. The stars were still bright against the darkness of the early morning sky. It was cold and a fresh breeze brushed around his black curly hair. He was wondering what to do. He closed the door as he went back into the farm cottage and up the small ladder to the loft bedroom where his wife was still in bed. She sat up.

'What's it like outside? she asked.

'A bit blustery,' he said, 'but it's our last chance before Christmas to sell our butter and pork at the fair. Are you feeling well enough to go?'

'No I'm afraid I'm feeling sick again. Could you possibly fetch me an empty chamber pot before you leave?'

'Of course my love. You stay in bed and keep yourself warm today and I'll bring you a sweetmeat back from the fair. I've got our wares ready packed and the list we wrote last night.'

He and Ann had married after the harvest in mid September. Together they farmed the small fields at Ty'n Llwden near Aberffraw which were his share of the inheritance following the death of his father. He was fortunate to have learned to read and write and was hopeful that his literacy skills would bring him opportunities to augment his meagre income. But he was concerned about his wife's sickness which she'd recently been experiencing, although she assured him that she would be better by lunchtime. He kissed her tenderly on the forehead and bade her farewell.

He was to meet up with several friends and neighbours at the crossroads near Hermon, where the horse and cart would be waiting. It would take almost an hour to reach the Abermenai point where one of the several ferries left Anglesey for Caernarfon. He laced up his sturdy leather boots and put on his greatcoat. He turned up the collar and set off.

By late morning Ann was feeling better. She got out of bed and pulled on her thick skirt and bodice and fastened her woollen shawl around her shoulders. She fanned the embers in the wide hearth and put on more sticks. Then she pinned a blanket over her shawl and went outside to gather eggs and feed the chickens and pigs. She wished now that she had gone with Hugh to the winter fair. She loved browsing around the market stalls and meeting relatives and friends. And she wondered if Hugh would remember to buy her favourite lace for the tablecloth.

The day dragged. By the afternoon the wind was strengthening and blowing from a south westerly direction, and whistling around the house. Ann had already prepared the potatoes and onions for supper. They were now simmering in the cast iron cooking pot which hung on a large hook over the fire. She lit the oil lamp and placed it on the table near some bunches of marram grass which were ready for weaving. She had learned the craft of basket- and mat-making from her mother, who still lived in the New Borough, and she was hoping to sell her best work at the fair day next spring.

The light was beginning to fade and the ferry would have left Caernarfon by now. She put more sticks on the fire and heard the wind buffeting the slated roof that Hugh and his brothers had recently completed. When would he be back? Perhaps he would call on his widowed mother on his way home. She couldn't wait to see him and what he had brought back for her.

Hours later there was still no sign of Hugh. Had something happened to him at the fair? Had he missed the ferry? Had the ferry capsized? She began to fear the worst. How could she live without him especially now that she was surely with child. She climbed the wooden steps and got into the big bed but the cold empty space on her left added to her despair. She tossed and turned and shivered throughout the long night and was up well before dawn the next day. The sickness had returned. She knelt on the rough matting and prayed to God to bring her husband safely back to her. She tried to keep busy to stop herself from worrying but lack of sleep overtook her and she sat at the kitchen table resting her head on her arms.

Suddenly the door opened and Hugh was there. He was empty handed and looked gaunt.

'Oh my darling, thank goodness you're back,' she cried and rushed up to him, wrapping her arms tightly around him. 'Where have you been? Whose coat are you wearing?'

He slumped by the fire and held his head in his hands. 'There's been a terrible tragedy.'

'What's happened?' Ann asked gently.

He took a deep breath and then sighed. 'We got into the ferryboat later than planned. The ferrymen had blown their horns by the castle walls to signal the boat's departure but most of the passengers were still amongst the crowds enjoying themselves and the tide was turning. We did leave before dark and the ferrymen tried to steer the boat along the deep channel near the Caernarfon side but a ferocious south westerly gale swept the boat onto Traeth Gwylltion.

Ann knew all about these dangerous shifting sands which lay midway between Anglesey and the mainland. 'Oh my goodness,' she said. 'Were the waters rising?'

'Yes. I'd travelled with Thomas Coledock who is a gardener on the Bodorgan estate. You remember him? We grew up together. Well, when the boat was swamped by the waves we got out onto the sandbank. Everyone followed us. We walked to and fro to keep warm and we shouted for help. It was awful to hear the screaming from the women and children. At first we were hopeful of a rescue but it was obvious the other boats would be putting themselves at great risk. It was a most heartrending sight to see them so close and yet so powerless to help.'

'What a dreadful thing to happen,' said Ann.

'We were all terrified. We knew the tide was rising fast and would cover the banks and we would surely drown. I knew I'd perish in those turbulent waters if I did nothing. My comrades were stricken with fear. They were bitterly cold and wretched. I suggested to Thomas that we make a raft by lashing an oar to the mast and using this to help us swim for the Anglesey shore. He had bought some straw rope at the fair which we used. But at the last minute he lost his nerve and was shivering uncontrollably. You see, he had never learned to swim.'

'Oh dear,' said Ann, 'I wonder what happened to him?'

'I don't know,' Hugh said, choking back a sob, 'I sadly embraced my dearest friend and he gave me his pocket watch for safe-keeping. Then I took off my heavy greatcoat and boots, tied myself to the makeshift raft and plunged into the stormy seas. You know I've little fear of the water but I still needed all my courage to throw myself into that raging sea. Somehow I reached the shore. My thoughts were always of you, my dear wife, and this gave me the strength to carry on.' He looked into her eyes and they held each other tightly.

After a while he continued. 'I was so relieved when I felt the firm ground beneath my feet but I could barely move my limbs. They were leaden and numb with cold and fatigue so I lay down to rest near a bare hawthorn hedge. I was soaking wet and starting to shake. I knew I had to go on so I dragged myself along the shoreline towards a lighted window. It was Foel ferry house. I banged on the door. The woman who opened it screamed in fright when she saw me. I was taken into the house and given brandy. My sodden clothes were removed and I was tucked into a warm bed. I remember very little more apart from the hot bricks by my feet.'

'Oh how very kind of them,' said Ann.

'Yes they did so much for me and even gave me this coat. They saved my life but I fear many others have been lost.'

Footnote – Hugh Williams was the only survivor out of 50 passengers. The boat was never found but his greatcoat and boots were discovered under a light covering of sand in the place he had left them.

THE PHOTOGRAPH
by Geoffrey Lincoln

In that far off summer
when past and future
were of little consequence,
sufficient was the joy
of a fleeting moment.

No breeze remains
to move your dark hair,
no scent of bluebells,
no skylark's song
to grace the morning.

Just a photograph
that's all
and memories inviolate,
untouched by time's
relentless passing.

A tiny window
casually left open;
a glimpse of our eternity
enhanced by the charm
of your innocence.

FOR FATHER'S SAKE
by Chris Pritchard

T he wind blew great veils of grey rain across the Menai Straits, blotting out the distant mountains as the ancient taxi crawled across Telford's Bridge. It stopped outside the hotel and a single passenger, a small woman wearing a voluminous brown mackintosh got out. She sighed as she looked up at the name of the hotel, The Anglesey Arms. It held so many memories for her particularly as one of her father's favourite haunts where he loved to write. The driver unloaded her large suitcase and battered briefcase and was surprised when she handed him a 10 shilling note and refused any change. That was more than twice the fare from Bangor station.

Megan struggled with the revolving door, dripping rain from her mackintosh, and hauled her luggage over to reception. The hotel smelled as she remembered, of a mixture of polish and cigarette smoke. A young man, wearing a tight starched collar, looked up and immediately recognised her. 'Your reservation Madame,' he quickly offered her the registration book to sign and handed over the keys to the best room. 'Would you like dinner this evening?' and when she nodded, he also gave her a large vellum envelope. 'This was left for you this afternoon. I'll have the luggage taken up to your room.' She thanked him, noting that the whole exchange had taken place in English. There was a long way to go before her first language had its rightful status in Wales.

She crossed the lounge to sit beside the roaring fire, pausing only to order a whisky and soda from the waiter. Ensconced in her chair she loosened her mackintosh, took a deep draft of whisky, and opened the envelope.

Dear Madame,

Thank you for taking time out of your busy schedule to visit your constituency. (Was there a hint of sarcasm there?) You will be pleased to know that your proposed visit to our new housing development at Tyddyn Isel, Menai Bridge, will take place at 10.30 a.m. prompt on Tuesday 29th April 1951. Mr Bevan will be joining us on site directly from the Station. Mr Alwyn Humphreys, Chairman of Housing, will collect you from your hotel at 10 a.m., and be your escort. Please refer any queries to him.

Yours faithfully,
Wilfred Bewley-Jones
Clerk to the Council

She smiled. Having been an M.P. for over 21 years, she remained amazed at the pomposity of local bureaucracy. But not for much longer she mused. Her star, like that of the Liberal Party, was on the wane and she would find it hard to secure the next election. At 49 she had much of her working life ahead of her so what to do if she lost her seat? Politics was her lifeblood and she would be lost without it.

Megan slept badly, her mind plagued with the dilemmas that

she knew were to face her shortly. By 10 a.m. however, she was ready in reception, neatly dressed in a navy woollen dress, a camel coat and a hat to match. Her anxious escort, Mr Humphreys, was on time and for some minutes they sat while he briefed her about the visit. He relaxed visibly when she responded to him in Welsh and the nervous tic below his left eye stopped. They were to tour the new housing development, meet the contractor and the local councillor and then have tea with a family who had recently been given a tenancy. The Press would be present.

The weather was much improved, with a cloudy sky but no rain as they drove through the small town to Tyddyn Isel. Local people had turned out to see her and she even spotted some bedraggled bunting – a kindly thought. The 'estate' was small, an oval of two-up, two-down houses evenly spaced around a large grassed area. Megan was reminded of her maiden speech, 21 years ago, when she had made an impassioned plea for better rural housing. It had taken time but this was the fruit of her efforts perhaps?

The obligatory pleasantries were observed as she talked to the contractor and local councillor before a second car, a large Bentley, drew up and a tall, round faced man emerged. The Right Honourable Nye Bevan was a formidable Labour innovator and a good friend to Megan. Together they toured the site, asking appropriate questions and praising the development which was hailed as one of the most important projects to help the under-privileged in post-war Wales.

At last, Mr Humphreys timidly intimated that they should move on and guided them into No 14 where the Hughes family was waiting. Alun and Ellen Hughes were wearing their best Sunday clothes and a china tea set had been borrowed for the occasion. The little house was spick and span with the smell of fresh baking emanating from the scullery and the inevitable flight of ducks above the mantelpiece. Taid Hughes sat in the corner by the fire, his wheezy chest troubling him. Ellen bravely gave Megan a tour. She noted the new, separated coal/wash-house, the indoor lavatory and the makeshift curtain in one bedroom to give 14-year-old Gladys some privacy from her younger brother, Eric. Taid slept in the box-room. Nye Bevan spoke with Alun Hughes, asking after his work at the newly set-up Saunders Roe plant locally and about the health of his father. A photograph of their eldest son Robert proudly displayed on the mantelpiece was duly admired. Robert was undertaking his National Service.

Having gathered in the living room, Gladys and 11-year-old Eric came in with a large plate of welshcakes and *bara–brith*. Tea was served and Megan and Nye did their best to keep the conversation with their over-awed hosts flowing. Megan concentrated her attention on Gladys, a lively looking dark-haired girl with NHS spectacles. Asked what she wanted to do after leaving school, Gladys took a surreptitious look at her mother before replying,' Work in the clothing factory like all me friends.'

'Are you doing well at school?' The question was too much for the proud father, who blurted out, 'Gladys has been top of her class for the last three years!'

'What about a place at college then?' Nye Bevan asked. There was an embarrassed silence before the father muttered, 'Costs too much ...' Wisely the subject was dropped, and after thanks for the hospitality, the VIPs departed.

Later, in the dining room of the Anglesey Arms, Megan's worried face troubled Nye.

'Are you concerned about your seat?' he asked gently.

Megan shook her head. 'I shall lose it this time, I have no doubt. The Liberals will diminish and I will have no avenue for the reforms I have fought so hard for. Who will champion the cause for families like the Hughes we saw today? Provide rural housing, employment, health care, and the opportunity for girls like Gladys to extend their education? I want Wales to be a vibrant country, using its native language and having a say in its own governance.'

Nye Bevan looked thoughtful for a moment. 'Your beliefs have always overlapped those of my own party – the Labour Party. Would it be such sacrilege to your father if you changed your allegiance in the interests of furthering your, and ultimately his, political ideals?'

Megan stared at her coffee, the milky sheen of the surface capturing her attention as his words pierced her heart but brought a smile of optimism to her lips. Somehow, she would continue as her father's heir.

Footnote – Megan Lloyd George, youngest daughter of former Prime Minister David Lloyd George, was M.P. for Anglesey from 1929–51, and the first woman M.P. in Wales. She lost the 1951 election as an Independent Liberal Democrat but became the Labour M.P. for Carmarthen in 1955. She served the people of Carmarthen up until her death in 1966. Her visit to Menai Bridge with Aneurin Bevan in 1951 was a turning point in her long and distinguished political career.

DRYCH
gan Gwyn M Lloyd

Hen brofiad cas wrth basio – ydyw gweld
Y gwydr yn fy nhwyllo.
Rhyw henwr a geir yno.
Nid wyf yn ei nabod o.

WE ARE THE OLD
by JMM

For Meals on Wheels we quietly wait –
for knock on door or click of gate.
We held high office in our day
but now, disabled, bent and grey
We can only sit and wait.

We are the old, it is our fate
to sit, immobile, vegetate.
We love your visits, lunch on tray.
Meals on Wheels.

We're put to bed at half past eight
like children, but we lie in late –
'til carer comes we have to stay.
We cannot sleep but know the day
has one bright spot, at any rate
Meals on Wheels.

LLANDDONA WITCH
by Owen Richard Jones (age 11)

I t was a stormy winter's night in Llanddona, with the wind howling and the waves smashing against the rocks. I picked up my candle and peered through my window into the darkness, I could see a shape in the distance. My mother came in.

'I can see something at sea,' I whispered.

'Go back to sleep Owen. There would be nothing out in this storm' she replied.

'But Mum ...'

'No Owen, sleep.' So back to bed I went.

By the morning the wind had died down. I gave myself a little stretch. I thought that I had dreamt it all until I opened the curtains and gazed through the window. I was shocked to see a big ship had drifted ashore and was wrecked on the rocks. I ran downstairs shouting.

'Mum, Dad, you won't believe it! I wasn't dreaming there was a ship on the rocks'. My mother looked outside to see the ship. My father told us to stay put as he knocked on the neighbour's door so they could approach the ship together. I had never seen a shipwreck before. As the news of the wreck travelled through the village, people gathered together and walked down the hill armed with reaping hooks and pitchforks. I followed the crowd, holding my mother's hand as my father was in the front with the braver farmers and villagers. As we approached the ship we could see it was badly damaged.

Suddenly there was a scream from the front of the crowd. I couldn't see what it was as I was too small but I felt very frightened. My mum picked me up. She was trembling now. I could see what was happening. I could see a person on the deck of the ship. I was not sure if it was a man or a child. It had red hair and a beard like a man but was only four foot tall. Its clothes were old, wet and bloodstained. Suddenly it collapsed but no one moved a muscle, we were all shocked. I asked my mother 'What is that?' She was too shocked to say anything.

Abruptly a large woman appeared on deck with a very strange eye and a long stick in her right hand. The crowd started shouting and refused to let her on land but she took no notice of them. She walked off the ship and shouted some words that I did not understand. Soon she was on the sand. She shouted some more then raised her stick. By now the crowd had backed down. They had never seen such an ugly woman before.

She plunged her stick into the sand, I could feel the ground shaking underneath my feet and then a gush of clear spring water shot high up into the air. We stood looking on in amazement. Someone in the crowd shouted, 'That is witchcraft!' I noticed it was my Uncle Goronwy ap Tudor. The crowd separated as he walked to the front. He told the farmers not to harm the visitors as they could cast a spell on them.

As I went to bed that night I looked through the window to see that these strange people had set fire to the ship with the dead bodies still inside. I could see the ship drift out to sea as the tide rose and then it sank. I could hear my uncle talking as I lay in bed that night. He was telling my mum and dad to be careful and to hang a horse shoe on the front door and sprinkle holy water around the house to protect it from the evil spirits. I felt that this was the start of a big disaster.

One day I went to the field to get some carrots for my mother and I met a little girl. She told me her name was Short Betty. She was very friendly and she had two thumbs on her right hand but I thought nothing of it. That night I told my mum that I had met a little girl named Short Betty but my Uncle Goronwy could hear me tell my mum as he was in the parlour with my father. He came through the door in a flash and told me off and said, 'Never talk or play with witches.'

Times were hard for these people, as they could not get water or food. On market days they would come to the village and demand food from the market stalls. The market men would give them food but the shipwreck people would not pay, as they had no money. The market men were frightened to say anything in case they cast a spell on them or their family. There was a very strange atmosphere in the village.

The leader of the tribe, the one who had cast a spell on the beach on that very first day, had built herself a little hut at Cadreddi near the beach. She was nicknamed Big Bella. I think she was the witch, she was never seen at the market but still she managed to survive somehow.

Strange things started to happen in the village. Potatoes, carrots and turnips started to disappear from the fields and cattle started to die in the fields at night. Even my uncle, Goronwy ap Tudor, who lived at Tarellwen farm experienced these strange goings on. It seemed that all the milk had been sucked out of the cattle until they started to bleed to death. Uncle Goronwy was not happy about this. Very soon, the villagers started to ask for advice but he had no idea what to do.

At night the farmers and villagers started to go out to the fields, with lamps, to see if they could get an answer to what was going on, but they had no luck. They could never catch anybody. All the villagers got very wary of the shipwreck people. The trouble must have been because of Bella and the shipwreck people. Even the little girl that I had met, Short Betty, must have been a witch just like uncle said. I was having supper with my uncle one night at Tarellwen when I asked if I could go with him round the fields with the dogs.

'Of course you can Owen if you're brave enough' was his reply. So we waited until darkness before going out with the other farmers and Jack the spaniel. I carried the lamp. It was a clear frosty night with a full moon and not a gust of wind. We could see far over the fields. I felt brave and courageous but my freezing hands holding the lamp tightly were gripping it with fear. As we went through the potato fields we saw that there were signs of fresh digging, as if some sort of animal had been scratching the earth. Uncle Goronwy shouted, 'We're close tonight lads we will get this beast if it's the last thing we do'.

We walked onwards up to the cattle fields. I got very frightened but wasn't prepared to show Uncle Goronwy. The fields were very steep and my legs were aching. All of a sudden my uncle put up his hand, I stood still. Jack had picked up a scent. Looking closely I could see a hare sucking on the cow's udders. Uncle Goronwy knelt down on one knee and aimed his gun. He shot the hare in the leg. She ran and vanished into the night. After that night no more cattle were killed on the fields. Everyone was hoping that the curse had been lifted from Llanddona.

A few days later my uncle came over for a cup of tea. He told my father that he was going to visit Big Bella. My mother pleaded with him not to go but he was determined to go and sort everything out. So off he went. He would not let anybody go with him to Carneddi where she lived. We waited for him to come back for hours. My mother kept on peering through the window. She was terrified for his safety. After a while we could hear a dog barking. I ran to the door. It was Jack coming up the land with Uncle Tudor. He came in and sat down by the fire.

'It's all sorted. The cattle will not die anymore. It was her, Big Bella,' he said.

'What do you mean?' I asked.

'Bella was sitting in the kitchen with bandages covered in blood on her leg. I told her I knew that she had been turning herself into a hare. She has now agreed not to cast any more spells on the village and never to kill any more cattle if I help her with her wounds,' he explained. From that day onwards the people of the shipwreck and the villagers managed to live together in harmony and I finally got to play with Short Betty.

BENLLECH IN WINTER
by Hilary Corning

My heart's in Benllech,
Where a shadowy winter moon
And fiery sun
Slowly change places
In a darkening sky.

Where the foothills
Of the mountains
Rise slowly to
Purple Snowdonia heights
Transformed by winter snows.

Where the waves
Slowly sweep
On an arc of sands
Sweeping from Benllech
To Llanddona.

My heart's in Benllech
Where fiery crimson
Streaks above black mountains,
In the joy of dawn.

My heart's in Benllech
Where friendly faces
Smile and share a joke,
And where helpfulness
Is just a way of life.

And when my life's
End draws nigh,
May I go in December,
And rest forever
Under the starry skies
Of Benllech in winter.

FOG
by J Downs

Sea and shore are lost,
shrouded in looming mystery.
Fog on Benllech beach

Then, disembodied,
gulls shrill shrieks overhead
break the fog's silence.

THE CIRCLE
by Bob Mason

We bought Bryn by accident. You see, Bob got the sack from Butlers after twenty years. They did give him a fifty thousand pounds golden handshake and as we've never owned a house we decided to get on the property ladder.

We went on holiday to Silver Bay. We had Mark, our twelve year old with us and one day we went into Llangefni to see some properties in Pritchard's window. There was an auction that afternoon at two o'clock. Well, we went to it and when we left an hour later we were the proud owners of a small-holding at Parc. Mark was disgusted and upset at the thought of losing his friends and going to a Welsh school. Also I didn't take to our new property. I don't know what it was but the moment we pushed open the rusty gate and walked towards the partial ruin it felt creepy, Mark felt it too and refused to explore. He just sat in the car sulking.

We had to leave the company's house by the end of the month. On the great day, the last day of June, I drove our battered Austin, towing our little caravan. Bob led the way in the hired van. In spite of himself, Mark was excited. How we managed to get all our stuff packed up I shall never know.

We wanted to make the house habitable before winter so, whilst we lived in the caravan, Bob set to with a will and worked from dawn to dusk. It was very exciting. The first job was to

clear years of overgrowth. We stripped the ivy-clad walls and cut down the old trees, letting in light and air. To our surprise Mark made himself useful, fetching and carrying. I was in charge of getting materials and soon I was immersed in paper work. Bob hired a local labourer to help with repairs to the roof but he didn't last. Neither did the next man, nor the next. In the end I put on overalls too. Mark and I became Bob's labourers.

We seemed to be dogged by bad luck. Each morning the trailer had a flat tyre. Then the well rope broke so we had no water until Bob got a long ladder and retrieved the bucket. It was a new rope too and seemed to have been cut about half way down which was odd. Then we had a terrible gale. The winds shrieked round the house all through the night. In the morning the garden was littered with debris. A branch had dropped on the roof of the car and the chimney pot had crashed through the slates. I cried as we tried to make breakfast. We then discovered that the gas had run out even though the Calor bottle was only two days old. The funny thing about that gale was it was so local. They said that the winds on the rest of the island were light. I could go on and on in this vein. Almost every day we had to contend with some inexplicable set back. Bob is naturally cheerful, an optimist, but even he began to crumble under the weight of our bad luck

We made three rooms habitable. We had running water from a pump Bob had installed and gas heating. The kitchen and bedroom and what was to be our living room were really nice but there was still a lot to do. The staircase was steep and needed replacing.

On our first night in the house, I was woken by a crash from the kitchen. I went in to see our teapot lying on the floor in pieces. Bob got up too and whilst we were surveying the mess we heard another noise from the bedroom. There, right in the middle of our bed, was a lump of ceiling plaster. Every week there was something amiss and the incidents happened mainly at night.

Worse was to come. Mark woke in the night screaming. Every night he had nightmares. He ran into our room and cuddled up with me. He said a horrible man had taken his duvet. We found it the next morning, screwed up into a bundle in the outside privy. We lived like this for five months. Bob made a new staircase – a beauty in polished pine. No sooner was it finished than a tin of white paint crashed on to it. That was a turning point in our troubles because now I knew that this was not a coincidence. I told Bob that the pot of paint was nowhere near the stairs when we went to bed. He remained unconvinced and we had our first tiff. He thought I was to blame. Until then I hadn't believed in ghosts but I got a book from the library and began to change my mind.

I decided to set a trap for this entity (I didn't like to think we were haunted). I did it all without Bob's knowledge because I knew he would pooh-pooh my idea. I left a china ornament on the edge of the window ledge. Sure enough in the morning it was on the floor. Mark began to cry and said he wouldn't live in the house any longer and would sleep in the caravan. The next morning he was hysterical. He'd had another nightmare about a boy being buried.

Over the next few nights I set things up for my little friend so that he would be tempted to more mischief. I placed another paint tin on the stairs. It crashed down like the last only this time it was empty. My next move was to catch him in the act. By this time I had given my 'poltergeist' (I got that out of the library book) a name. I called him Horace. I rigged up a chain of mirrors so that I could see my next trick even though it was in the kitchen and I was in bed. I decided to sacrifice an old vase. I made it difficult for Horace by putting it at the back of a kitchen unit and then hiding everything else in the cupboards and tying the doors with string. That night I lay awake. Nothing seemed to happen but in the morning the string on the doors was untied.

I got him in the end though. It was a full moon and I don't know what woke me but when I saw the vase moving across the counter the hairs on the back of my neck bristled. I nudged Bob awake and together we watched it slide by itself to the edge and then crash to the floor. Bob was out of bed like a bullet. He switched on the light but there was nothing to see. We walked around the house and, then putting on coats, went outside. The garden was bathed in moonlight. We could see to the end of the field. We stood in stunned silence. What we saw was a stone circle. Each of twenty stones was illuminated as if from inside. In the centre was a large flat stone. As we watched, a cloud covered the moon and the scene faded. I wanted to get a torch and investigate but Bob wanted to get back to bed. He said it could wait till morning.

At eight I was up and dressed. I went out to the field. The

stone circle had disappeared. After breakfast Bob got a spade. He could remember where the stones were. After turning over a few sods he found the first. He dug all day and by tea time had uncovered most of the stones but some premonition told him not to dig at the centre. Mark kept saying, 'I want to go home', meaning Rochdale.

A week later we went to Llangefni, shopping. On our return our house was alight. Our neighbours had called the brigade but by the time they arrived it was hopeless. I told the *Daily Post* the whole story thinking they might be interested enough to pay a fee. The local vicar visited us in the caravan to ask if we needed help. He had read our tale in the *Post* and thought that the flat stone needed investigation. We were astonished when he returned the next day, complete with his 'bell, book and candle' so to speak, but also with a JCB. He soon found the flat stone, three feet down. Under it was the skeleton of a boy.

That is why we sold Bryn for half what we had paid. The following summer we went back to see the ruin we had left. The house was rebuilt. The family living there just laughed at us when I mentioned the word 'haunted'. That's the end of our sad tale. We moved back to Rochdale. It doesn't seem quite as smoky as it used to and Bob is on the look-out for another job.

PENRHOS CLOSE
by Kim Jones

Mrs Jones at No. 1,
Poor soul, has an adolescent son
With the muckiest bedroom I've ever seen.
His Mum's too scared to go in and clean.

The Williamses at No. 2,
They take a different point of view.
Her hours of polishing the floor
Makes him leave his boots outside the door.

The Minister lives at No. 3.
Pens his sermons over tea.
He's been strict 'Chapel' all his life
But the woman he lives with is not his wife.

Old Mrs Morgan, No. 4.
Closes the curtains and bolts the door,
Counts her pension in a biscuit tin
And drinks black coffee, laced with gin.

At No. 5, lives Miss Lovelace.
She hangs her washing in a pillowcase
So that the neighbours will not stare
At her selection of men's underwear.

Two gentlemen live at No. 6 –
The plastic planters and coloured bricks.
In the backroom of these nice old boys
You should see their collection of 'adult toys'.

The grumpy old man at No. 7,
May have already gone to Heaven.
Broken window and missing slate
But who's going round to investigate?

Poor Mr Hughes at No. 8,
His wife has left. He's in a state.
Asking the neighbours: 'Has anyone seen her?'
He should have asked me – the window cleaner!

THE BENCH
by Janet Pritchard

Y ou may have looked at me in the past when my paint was blistered and peeling, my legs wobbly and caked with grime, my bolts rusted and broken, and said to yourself 'Just a useless piece of junk, throw it on the scrap heap.' That is if you even thought of me at all – but I'm not junk, really I'm not. I'm not like all other cheap benches that you find in the stores these days – I am special! I have a history. Do I hear a scornful laugh? Please don't. I've seen so many things in my lifetime, things I would like to share with you before I end my days. Can you spare me a little time, to listen to my story? You can? Then please be seated.

I wasn't made in a factory. Oh no! I was carefully hand crafted out of solid teak by a carpenter. If you look carefully at my slats, you can see that they are shaped for your comfort, the timber curved, hewn to perfection. I was made for a ship named *Caesarea* and she was built in 1960 in the Isle of Wight, and launched on January 29th. She then spent the next few months being fitted out for passengers.

She wasn't an ocean going giant but represented a step up from other lesser vessels. She had five decks and a single funnel. You should have seen me then, bolted to the deck and gleaming. Passengers used to sit on me and I would listen to them and feel all their emotions, happy and sad.

I will always remember *Caesarea's* maiden voyage from Weymouth. It was the 16th November 1960 and the weather was bitterly cold. Since this was a special trip, we had only invited guests on board and one came to sit on me. She didn't stay long because of the weather but the pride of that moment lives with me still. When we arrived in Jersey other ships greeted us with blasts and sirens and the tug, *Duke of Normandy*, dressed with flags and pennants, was there to assist us into the harbour but the captain eased her in with no trouble. Oh! The unadulterated pride of that moment!

On 2nd December 1960, we made our first commercial voyage and although not full, it seemed to me as if there were passengers everywhere. So began my years back and forth from Weymouth to Jersey. They seem a blur now. Mostly I remember the passengers for I have been witness to many things - to sea sickness, sadness, arguments, proposals, stolen kisses and even to illicit plans. I could go on and on, but to tell you all the stories would be indiscreet and I pride myself on keeping the secrets. There was adventure too. In August 1968 the ship was holed coming into Weymouth harbour in bad weather and was sent to Southampton for repair.

In February 1971 the ship went for a refit to change her livery from British Rail to Sealink and I was retired and sold for scrap. Would you believe it – me scrap? I was bought by a member of staff, for the grand old sum of £2.00 which, to be fair, was quite a sum of money in those days. I heard later that on the 6th October 1975, the *Caesarea* made her last trip to the Channel Islands. She had made 2,042 round trips, had steamed 396,148 miles and had carried 3,267,000 passengers and I am proud I was part of her history.

I was put to rest in a garden and my wood was covered in brown paint. I suppose I looked reasonably tidy but I was neglected for many years. This time is a bit hazy, to be honest. At some stage I was taken by lorry, together with furniture and other goods, to a village called Llanfairpwllgwyngyll. Again, I was put in a pleasant garden; occasionally another coat of paint was slapped over me. The kind gentleman and his wife would sit on me and drink their coffee on a summer's morning and I would greatly enjoy these moments as I listened to their conversation. Then, only his wife would come and I could sense her grief and sadness. Later, no-one came and so I rotted there for many years. It looked as if my story was at an end.

Then in 2011, I was removed from that garden and taken to another village called Menai Bridge and I was pulled apart. I confess that at the time I thought that I was being broken up to be thrown away. But no – all my wood was stripped down and the beautiful teak, which had been covered with blistered paint for so many years, was rediscovered. All the rusty bolts were thrown away and replaced with shiny new ones. The rust was removed from my rickety old legs and they were painted silver.

Look at me now! Don't I look wonderful? My wood has been oiled and I gleam. I am not on a ship (things are never perfect!) but in a garden. There are flowers everywhere, my owner comes to sit on me every dry day and when visitors come, they sit on me and again I happily listen to their conversation.

I am over fifty years old now and as good as new. I believe I have at least another fifty years ahead of me. I guarantee that I will outlive you and I can only daydream about my future.

'This seat is an heirloom.' my owner once said to her son as they sat side by side.

'Don't worry, I'll look after it when you've gone Mum,' he answered.

Whether he will, time will tell. For the present, I am content with my world.

WASHI BACH –
TRIBUTE TO A TRAMP
by Georgina Parker

The seasons foretold his presence,
Returning to the autumn airs of Môn.
Straggly beard, hedge-row slept clothes,
'Mornin' missus', holding out a gnarled hand
For a comforting can of tea.

Sometimes with ragged dog or skinny horse,
His creature comforts in the darkening nights
Oft alone, combing the green lanes,
For the sight of a warm barn.

No real material needs, save bread and tea,
Taking his solitary pleasures from the land,
The seascapes, woods and quiet fields,
Reliant on nature for his annual round.

Welcomed through the villages,
A bird of good-omen – *y cymeriad*,
Reassuring all of the turning world,
And the predictability of the seasons.

But the cold wind of change had to blow
Across the winter ridges of Ynys Môn
And Washi grew too gaunt to walk
The well remembered paths he loved.

And yet, his independent spirit soars
Above the landscape that he loved so well,
And we recall those tales he sowed,
Our hero of the open road.

MAE GEN I DEIMLAD
gan Ffion Wyn Jones (14 oed)

Mae fy meddwl ym mhobman –
Ofnaf gymryd cam.
Asennau yn deilchion,
Cleisian yn fapiau clwyfus!
Dim rhyddid i chwerthin na siarad.
A oes cariad yn y byd?
Neu ydy rhieni pawb 'r un peth o hyd?

Rwy'n enaid di-hyder yn byw mewn ofn,
Fel morgrugyn yn gyfyng mewn cornel!
Fan yma oedd fy ngenedigaeth,
A fan yma bydd fy marwolaeth.

Mae gen i deimladau.

Ymlusgo i fyny'r grisiau,
Wedi'r gweiddi byddarol.
Ai dim ond fi sy'n cael fy nhrin fel llwch?
Neu ydi plant bach eraill yn yr un cwch?

Mae gen i deimlad.

NOT GOING ANYWHERE
by Kay Middlemiss

There is a house on Anglesey that has a rather unusual feature. The entire wall of one room is a painted mural. (It's not the house you are thinking of but there is a connection.)

This house recently came into the hands of a wealthy man from the Midlands who thought it would be ideal for weekend house parties and corporate entertaining. And so it was.

The man from the Midlands was not a connoisseur of art but he did realise that he had something of unique interest in the garden scene on his dining room wall. The painting had been so cunningly designed and executed that it could have been a garden in almost any season of the year. There were lawns and paths, pergolas luxuriant with unidentified climbing plants, mature trees and a fishpond. In the foreground, near to the house, was a terrace with a table and two comfortable garden chairs, their plumped up cushions just asking to be occupied. In fact, the mural was so lifelike that when the host made his habitual after dinner joke: 'Shall we have coffee in the garden?' there was often one innocent guest who said yes, and wondered why everyone laughed.

However, in the eyes of its new owner the painting had one great flaw. The artist, recalling an incident concerning a more famous mural, had placed an ashtray on the table He had then painted such a realistic burning cigarette on its edge that viewers

110

had an almost irresistible urge to reach over and stub it out before it fell onto the table and caused some damage. In the days when nearly everyone smoked, this little whimsy would have merely raised a smile – the artist's private joke – but with today's anti-smoking attitude, the cigarette became a horror out of all proportion to the intention.

The man from the Midlands made fun of it by asking his dinner guests how they would deal with the potential problem. Suppose the cigarette were to fall out of the ashtray and set light to the lace tablecloth? But as the meal progressed and the good wine flowed freely, some of the suggestions became so outrageous that he feared for the safety of his mural. He decided on a radical solution.

The local artist hired to paint out the burning cigarette was reluctant to interfere with such a remarkable piece of art but recession was biting and he had not received a commission for some time. He named an exorbitant fee and was astonished when it was accepted.

Following his brief, the local artist carefully painted out the ashtray and its contents. Satisfied that he had done a good job, although still feeling like a vandal, he hand-delivered the bill the following weekend. The man from the Midlands was not amused.

'I pay my bills on completion not before the work is started.'

'But I did what you asked. I painted out the ashtray and the cigarette.'

'You did not. Come in and show me what you've done. The painting looks to me the same as it did last weekend.'

The artist could not believe his eyes. There, on the wall, was the burning cigarette almost at the point where it must fall out of the ashtray onto the table.

'That was not in the painting when I left it.' The artist was adamant but he could tell he was not being believed. 'I'll come back this afternoon and do it again. You can watch and maybe you'll believe me then.'

'I have to be in London this evening. My train leaves in half an hour. You can come back tomorrow. I shall expect a result when I'm here next weekend. I think you're an honest man so keep the house key. Perhaps you've been overworking?'

After a sleepless night worrying about his own sanity, the artist repeated his work on the mural. He knew he had painted out the ashtray. There must be some trickery going on. But why? Could it be an insurance fraud, something like that? The thing made no sense at all.

Once again he obliterated the offending cigarette. Then, as soon as it was dry, he painted over it once more, just to make sure it could not re-appear again.

But that is exactly what did happen. When the artist returned the following day – there it was – the cigarette still smouldering, the line of ash lying in the dish. It was as if the painting had never been touched. Now he knew there was some trickery going on. With the owner away the house was empty but someone must be able to come and go at will. He had been given a key. Who else had one?

By now the artist had decided it was not the owner who was behind the practical joke. The man from the Midlands was the victim not the perpetrator. So who was the second painter who could produce such a perfect replica of the original? Whoever it was, he was certainly a talented artist. That evening the artist paid a visit to a friend who worked for a specialist security company.

At lunchtime the next day, armed with a selection of recording and video equipment, burglar alarms and sensor lights which he placed in strategic positions about the room, the local artist began his third attempt to alter the mural. He watched over his work for the remainder of the day and when night came he settled down in an armchair to wait out the hours of darkness. The empty house grew cold and he was pleased he had remembered to bring a blanket and a flask of coffee.

At first, adrenalin kept him wide-awake and alert to every sound but, as he grew accustomed to the creaks and noises of the old house, his thoughts began to wander. He pictured the original artist painting his mural. Had he also spent nights, maybe in this same spot, contemplating his creation? Planning? Rejecting? Redesigning? Who had lived in the house then? Who had commissioned the mural? And why this room... Before he knew it the local artist was sound asleep.

First there was a flash then the click-whir of the video springing to life. Or was it the other way round? He could never quite remember the sequence of events, it was too bizarre.

Opening his eyes, his sleep-drenched brain registered a slim, dark haired, young man. The man's face was turned towards the mural so he could not see his features. Stumbling out of his chair, the local artist made a lunge towards the intruder. He had not seriously considered what he would do if he actually caught someone in the act but now the restraining blanket hindered him and by the time he was out of the chair the man had vanished.

The doors and windows remained firmly shut. The corridor was empty. He knew that old houses like this one often had concealed doors and hidden passages once used by servants, now probably unknown to their present owners.

It was not a problem though, he had the whole episode on video. Within hours the joker would be identified, the mystery solved and the man from the Midlands would apologise for his mistake. The local artist went back to his armchair, his blanket, and peaceful dreams.

The man from the security company was puzzled.

'I know it's none of my business but why did you hire all that equipment just to photograph a painting? A digital camera would have done the job.'

'I wasn't photographing the mural,' the local artist was impatient. 'I need to identify the man.' There was a slight pause. 'The man?'

'The young man standing in front of the painting. Don't tell me the camera didn't catch him?'

'Can't have done. You must have pointed it in the wrong direction. All I can see in the front of the picture are two chairs, a table with an ashtray and a burning cigarette. I must say it looks a bit dangerous.'

'If you can see that, then there must be a shot of the young man.'

'Sorry, nothing else in any of the frames, except ...'

'Except?'

'In the last shot, it looks like ... but it can't be, it's suspended in mid air. It looks just like a paint brush.'

So, patient reader, if you are invited to a dinner party on Anglesey you may find yourself in a room that has a garden mural on one wall. And, if you should spy an ashtray in the painting with a cigarette that is about to burn the tablecloth, don't be alarmed. It won't fall. It is not going anywhere.

EARLY MORNING DOG WALK
by JMM

The beach blooms white in the grey morning light.
Dog owners moonwalk across its surface,
padded clothing dark against the snow,
torchlight slicing the gloom.

Slithering on the icy slipway, I join them,
blinking away sleet and sharp sand.
Dogs, aerial-eared, face into the gale.

Striding against its fury,
through the spume of a monstrous sea,
a rosy streak in the sky
defines the black hills beyond.
One hint of colour on this bleak December day.

EGGING ON
by Alan Caldwell

'You haven't heard about it?' We were walking on the heather-clad slopes above the rugged shore to the south of Moelfre and we met a fascinating man. 'It was a dark and stormy night – it really was,' he said, 'the night of 25 October 1859, the night the *Royal Charter* foundered.' He said the words with a laugh, as though he relished the idea. 'Yes. Off the coast here. Hundreds of ships were wrecked in Liverpool Bay that night.'

We were fascinated by his personality. If he'd had a beard, he could have been the Ancient Mariner and I wanted to hear him telling the story. But the old man stooped to stroke the black Labrador. 'Name's Llewellyn.' My wife stroked the dog too.

The children were away, so we – just the two of us – were on a weekend break from Liverpool. It was a beautiful summer's day. Clear blue sky. Bright sunshine. The sea was that blue that summons artists to their best work. Sunlight shimmering on the surface and calm as could be. There was a warm and gentle breeze, off shore – that would make it south-westerly. We knew the place – we often came – and we had our walking boots on so the long spikes of heather were no problem.

The dog-walker wore a waxed anorak with a blue roll-neck jumper showing underneath. He could have been a seaman. 'Do you know much about it?' I said.

'Oh, yes. The vessel was out in the Atlantic, come from Australia. A fine three-masted clipper, but she had an amazing improvement – steam engines to use when there was no wind, the latest thing. So there was a funnel as well as sails.'

'A passenger ship?' I said, egging him on.

'Oh, yes. Hundreds of people on board, all carrying gold about their person. Miners coming back from striking it lucky. And a huge cargo of gold as well, thirty million in today's money, they say. A luxury clipper. Think what it was like standing on deck. The sound of the bow cutting through the water, swish-sh-sh' – he made the sound – 'and the bow wave spreading either side. The rustling of the sails on those three masts, as many as four sails on a single mast, cross-rigged. Not to mention the flying jibs. You'd hear the groaning of the yards against the masts. The creaking of the ship's timbers. Seagulls crying.'

My wife, Gwyneth, butted in. 'I thought the hull was iron.'

The nautical gentleman coughed. 'Ah, yes, but there'd be wooden parts as well.' He sat down. 'Me legs, you know.'

We sat as well, on the warm heather. The dog lay down, muzzle resting on its legs. 'Do go on,' I said. I was fascinated, not only by the graphic description but also by the narrator. His demeanour confident, eyes crinkly and voice fervent, as if he'd been there on board that day.

'The moon was out. A few passengers moving about the deck.' He said it with an eagerness that gave the picture tension. 'Lovers leaning on the taffrail, perhaps, watching the foamy wake and the phosphorescence. They'd been two months at sea.

'But there were dark clouds to the east.' He furrowed his brow, and there was a dramatic tremor in his voice. He'd have sounded ominous if he were only reading the bus timetable. 'On the bridge the mate studied the barometer. Can you imagine the conversation with the Master?'

'The glass is falling sir.'

'Don't worry, we can weather Anglesey and we'll be home in Liverpool before it gets serious.'

'You don't think we should put into Holyhead until it improves?'

The response was sharp: 'Are you telling me how to run my ship Mr Mate?'

'No, sir. I was just ...'

'The owners don't pay us to cower in port when there's a fresh breeze.'

'So they sailed on, making record headway, towards Anglesey where they would pick up the Liverpool pilot. But the wind changed to the north-east, and strengthened. The situation was perilous. There was no hope of taking the pilot on board. Can you imagine it? The wind shrieking in the rigging. Seamen aloft trying to furl the sails, but the wind rose to gale force. Spray sputtered on the electric lamps lighting the deck work. It was difficult to hear any orders that were given.'

'Mr Mate, have the lifeboats unlashed; ready to send away.'

'Aye-aye, sir.'

'Below, the steam engines throbbed. In the heat, stokers sweltered and shovelled coal into the boilers. They took off their shirts, and sweated in the glare of the fires. And still the bridge asked for more steam but the speaking tubes were sometimes neglected as everybody was toiling. They had shipped too much water but there was no power available to work the pumps.

'The wind rose to storm force. They were off a lee shore and being driven. She was a modern vessel. She had steam engines but they were only intended as auxiliary. At 11 p.m. they dropped both anchors but would they hold? The Master called for still more steam. With engines at full stretch, there was a chance they could ride out the storm.

'The order was given to cut down the masts to reduce the effect of the wind. The scene was chaotic. The waves enormous – high as the council offices in Llangefni, and they broke over the ship. The crew used bolt cutters to cut away the shrouds and stays so the masts could float free. But there was wire rigging everywhere. The whole ship juddered to and fro like a child's boat on a string in white water.

'At 1 a.m. there was an explosion like a gunshot and the ship lurched. It was the port anchor chain. It snapped and whipped onto the deck with the force of an express train and crashed through the deckhouse roof. The starboard bow of the clipper was now taking the force of the wind and the ship listed heavily to port. The waves were breaking over the ship and she was taking solid water on deck.

'There was another gunshot and the starboard anchor chain parted. This time, the bow, suddenly released, leapt up, with a sickening motion. The vessel slewed to port and now took the waves athwartships. She was driven onto a sandbank. Just over there.' He pointed generally out to sea. 'Nothing could save her now; she was finished. The tide rose and lifted her off the bank. The waves smashed her onto the rocks just here.' He indicated the shore below where we were sitting. 'It was like hell: the wind screaming; the ship rolling as wave after wave hit her; the heavy surf pounding on the rocks; the panic screaming of the passengers; and the ghastly shrieks of pain. The explosion and hiss of steam when the seawater hit the fires. Some jumped and tried to swim, but many were weighed down by the gold they had on them and drowned. Some tried to scramble through the surf but were pounded to death on the rocks. About five hundred people died. Only forty men survived; no women or children.

'Some were saved by a courageous Maltese crew member who swam ashore with a line. Ah, it was a tragedy sure enough. Worst in Anglesey history. But a boon to some. There are many tales about people suddenly becoming rich round here but most of them are rubbish. Certainly many people found pieces of gold around and not much was handed in. But remember, it wasn't only a matter of finding gold; it was often a case of removing the gold from dead bodies. A grisly affair. I don't know whether anybody was ever charged.

'It did change the lives of some. And it still has an effect today. There's young PJ, with his fleet of hire cars and fishing boats. They say his great-grandfather, who was church-mouse poor, suddenly bought two brand new fishing boats the following spring and, father-to-son, the business has done well ever since.'

'Is all this true?' I said.

'Oh, yes. Gospel! I mean, not about PJ.'

'But didn't the *Royal Charter* founder to the north of Moelfre, at Porth Alerth?'

'Well now … Maybe it did.'

'How did you get all this knowledge about it?'

'I was a guide for 'Go-with-us' holiday agency. They have tours all over North Wales. That was years ago. I'm eighty-seven now. Perhaps I do get things a bit wrong.'

'But you were so interesting. I was quite spell-bound. You must have been a really good tour guide.'

'Thought you said you hadn't heard of the *Royal Charter*.'

'No, I didn't say that. In fact, I did my M.A. dissertation on it at Bangor University!'

'I see … Enjoy the rest of your break … Come on Llewellyn.'

A WALK THROUGH THE FOREST

by Geoffrey Lincoln

Late September.
Odorous.
Damp.
Sunlight sifting
through the pines' tracery.

Arm-in-arm
we delight in the morning,
grasping the joy
of this enchanted moment.

Through your eyes
we discover treasures
overlooked by wanderers
preoccupied by daily cares:
delicate ferns –
frond upon tiny frond.
plump berries –
jet and ruby-red.
Trembling leaves –
gold-burnished.

You gather
the transient fragments
of a summer's splendour:
pink campion,
purple clover,
speedwell, blue.

Offering me a posy,
a gift before we part;
that I shall treasure
always.

LLYN CERRIG BACH
gan Eflyn Owen-Jones

Hanes darganfyddiad pwysig ym 1943, o greiriau Oes yr Haearn yn Llanfair-yn-Nhowyn, ger awyrlu'r Fali.

Yn Saesneg, cyfieithir enw'r llyn yma yn aml yn 'Lake of Little Stones' ond nid yw hyn yn gywir, gan yn wreiddiol, llyn ar dir tyddyn Cerrig Bach ydoedd. Felly'r dehongliad agosaf, fuasai'r llyn yn perthyn i Cerrig Bach.

Erbyn heddiw, mae'r llyn yn enwog drwy'r byd i gyd. Rwy'n falch o hyn, gan mai oherwydd penderfyniad fy nhad, William Roberts, i garthu'r tir corslyd ar Faes Awyr Y Fali amser yr Ail Ryfel Byd y daeth hyn i fod.

Oherwydd ei arbenigaeth mewn rheoli tir tywodlyd ar y cwrs golff gerllaw, cafodd fy nhad ei apwyntio gan yr Awyrlu yn bennaeth tir dros dîm o ddynion. Roedd angen gosod glanfeydd hirach ar gyfer awyrennau'r Americanwyr oedd am lanio yn Y Fali yn ystod yr Ail Ryfel Byd.

Er mwyn sefydlogi'r tir tywodlyd, cyn gosod y tarmac ar gyfer y glanfeydd, penderfynodd fy nhad mai'r peth doethaf i'w wneud oedd carthu gwaelod y corsydd oddi amgylch ac yna thaenu'r mwd mawnog ar y safleoedd.

Trefnodd gosod pwced haearn fawr, i drafeilio gyda chymorth injan stêm o un ochr o'r llyn i'r llall. Wedi iddi gyrraedd canol y llyn, roedd y bwced yn cael ei gostwng i waelod y dŵr a'i llusgo ymlaen gan gasglu i fyny'r pridd mawnog o'r gwaelod. Yna, roedd yn gorffen ei thaith drwy daflu ei chynnwys ar y lan yr ochr arall. Yno, roedd y mwd gwlyb yn cael ei adael i ddiferu rywfaint cyn i'r dynion ei rawio i mewn i lorri a'i gludo i safle'r glanfeydd.

Un diwrnod, fe aeth lorri yn sownd yn y mwd ac fe dorrodd y weiren a roddwyd ynghlwm wrth y tractor i geisio ei thynnu'n rhydd. Cofiodd fy nhad iddo weld yn gynharach yn y dydd, hen gadwyn yn gorwedd yn y mwd. Aeth i'w nôl a defnyddiwyd honno yn llwyddiannus i dynnu'r lorri'n rhydd. Mae gennyf recordiad o'm tad yn egluro fel y defnyddiwyd y gadwyn fwy nag unwaith yn ystod y dydd i wneud yr un dasg. Ar ddiwedd y dydd, gan ei fod yn gweld bod y gadwyn yn un mor anarferol, penderfynodd fy nhad ei dangos i beiriannydd yr orsaf, Mr J. Jones, oedd yn rhannu'r un swyddfa ag ef.

Roedd Mr Jones o'r De ac awgrymodd mai'r peth doethaf, oedd iddo wneud dyluniad o'r gadwyn a'i anfon gyda nodyn i'r Amgueddfa Genedlaethol yng Nghaerdydd i ofyn eu barn arni.

Ymhen dau ddiwrnod, roedd Sir Cyril Fox, y prif guradur, wedi dod i'r Fali. Gwelodd y gadwyn ac amryw o bethau eraill oedd wedi eu tynnu o'r mwd. Ei ganlyniad oedd nodi mai cadwyn ar gyfer caethweision neu garcharorion oedd hi, a'i bod tua 2,000 o flynyddoedd oed. Erbyn y diwedd, darganfuwyd oddeutu 150 o greiriau i gyd, ac roeddynt wedi eu taflu i'r llyn dros gyfnod o 200 mlynedd. Yn nodweddiadol, nid oedd yr un ohonynt yn deillio o amser y Rhufeiniaid ym Môn.

Yn eu mysg roedd cadwyn arall ychydig llai, plac a bôth tarian efydd, gwaywffon, cleddyfau, darnau o gerbydau rhyfel, sawl genfa ceffyl, barrau haearn cyfnewid, darnau o utgorn a chrochan a llawer o ddarnau diddorol eraill. Roedd y mwyafrif wedi dod o Loegr ac ambell un o'r Iwerddon.

Mae'r darnau efydd wedi eu haddurno gyda dyluniad Triskelé. Mae'r rhain yn cyfateb â dyluniadau tair tro troellog ar greiriau tebyg a ddarganfuwyd mewn llyn yn y Swistir. Dyma pam mae casgliad Llyn Cerrig Bach mor bwysig ac yn fyd enwog erbyn hyn.

Y darnau mwyaf nodedig yw'r cleddyfau sydd yn amlwg wedi cael eu plygu'n bwrpasol, bron yn eu hanner. Awgrymir gan wybodusion mai tystiolaeth yw hyn eu bod wedi eu taflu yn fwriadol i'r llyn fel offrwm. Yn ystod amser y Derwyddon ym Môn, roedd yna arferion fel taflu offrwm i Arglwyddes y Dŵr. Tybed mai llyn sanctaidd fel hyn oedd Llyn Cerrig Bach? Ydi'r darnau o grochan ac utgorn yn awgrymu rhan o ddefod tybed? Hefyd y waywffon hir a throm iawn, tybed fuasai hi wedi cael ei chario ar flaen seremoni?

Erbyn pan daflwyd y darnau olaf, roedd y Rhufeiniaid wedi croesi'r Fenai ac yn gorymdeithio i gyfeiriad Llyn Cerrig Bach. Yn ôl beth a ysgrifennwyd gan Tacitus, y cofnodwr Rhufeinig, eu bwriad oedd lladd y Derwyddon i gyd. Tybed ai taflu eu hoffrymau i'r llyn i ofyn i'w Harglwyddes eu hachub a wnaethant? Yn amlwg, ni weithiodd eu hymbil, gan i'r Rhufeiniaid lwyddo i ladd y Derwyddon i gyd a dinistrio'u hallorau. Efallai bod rhai o'r derwyddon wedi gallu ffoi i'r Iwerddon neu Ynys Manaw. Pwy a ŵyr?

RESCUE
by E Jones

The *Harold* was a 140ft steel-hulled steamship built in 1898, registered in Glasgow but owned by a Liverpool company.

The *Duke of Northumberland* was a 50ft lifeboat built in 1889. It was the first ever steam lifeboat and was of a revolutionary design. Water was drawn in through the hull and forced out at great pressure through the vents in the side of the boat. It was transferred from Harwich to Holyhead in 1892.

It was on 22 February1908 that the paths of two ships were to cross. The *Harold* was carrying a cargo of china clay from Teignmouth to Runcorn when it was caught in a west-north-westerly gale blowing upwards of 80 mph and gusting to 100 mph with tremendous seas. The ship's engine broke down when it was off Holyhead and distress signals were fired as the ship drifted between the dangerous headlands known as North and South Stack. Two anchors were let go and the crew awaited the arrival of the Holyhead lifeboat.

The location of the ship in distress was not a great distance from the lifeboat station and, as always, no time was wasted in getting the lifeboat underway. But a terrible sea was running that day and it was miraculous that the *Duke of Northumberland* was able to power its way through the storm. No other lifeboat of its time could have coped. It took two hours of the most skilful and hazardous manoeuvring by Coxswain William Owen and his crew before the lifeboat was able to get close enough to the Harold to pass a line across. Six crewmen were taken off. The rescue efforts continued and the lifeboat itself was in great danger of being flung against the steamer. Eventually, the lifeboat was able to make a pass sufficiently close for the remaining three crew members to jump aboard.

As a result of this heroic rescue Coxswain Owen was presented with the RNLI's highest gallantry award, a Gold Medal, by the Prince of Wales. The ten crew members, who included his son, all received silver gallantry medals.

One hundred years later, to commemorate this, one of the greatest rescues in Welsh RNLI history, the families of the crew of the *Duke of Northumberland* were taken by the current lifeboat and its volunteer crewmen to the exact spot where the *Harold* sank and the rescue took place. Once there, the engine was switched off and a prayer was said in memory of RNLI achievements and for those who have given their lives in its service. I was honoured to have been there. William Owen was my great-grandfather.

The RNLI is an independent charity and does not receive any funding from the UK government. The lifeboat crews are all volunteers, local men who deserve our gratitude and support.

PENMON LIGHTHOUSE
by Anne Bassett

When the first pink and gold fingers of dawn
Stroke away the last night clouds of puffy darkness
And touch my sea-spray dampened sides,
I will shut my rhythmic blinking eye
And languish in the soft warmth of daybreak.

I know that today will be a true summer's day
And I shall slumber in the sun's bright blanket,
Waking from time to time roused by cheerful sailors' calls
And the slap of stretched canvas,
As the shimmering yachts glide by.

All will marvel at my towering, tapering height
And my strong, elegantly slender body
Wearing the striking pattern of my uniquely fashioned dress.
Gleaming and proud I stand upon my rocky realm –
Unassailable, magnificent, indispensable.

HAELIONI

by Alan Wyn Roberts

Hydrefu'r coed yn Ebrill
Yw'n camp a'n gorchest ni,
Difwyno ffrwd a fforest,
Glafoerio oel i'r lli,
Er llygru byd mae llannerch werdd
A llwyn i'r llinos byncio'i cherdd.

Pan ddaw y gawod gynnes
I oglais blagur Mai,
A'r beichiog gloddiau gwyddfid
I berarogli'r clai;
Daw mantell nos a'i gwlithoedd mân
Ar bawb a phopeth heb wahân.

TILL THE LAND DIES
by David Turnbull

It was in the year of our Lord 560. The two holy men were very aware of time and date, they had journeyed to this same spot many times. On the new moon of each season, they had trudged along pathways that led them to this place deep in the heart of Môn.

In the beginning, they were young men, dedicated and fervent in their calling. Privations were many and accepted as a challenge in the worship of their belief. Now, age had joined them as they broke bread in preparation for their tiring walk home. They made their last vows together.

'Let us meet here again brother when the land itself shall die.'

They each planted a yew sapling to seal the bargain and embraced in a tearful farewell. Cybi watched the old man begin his journey eastward.

'Till the land dies, Seiriol my friend,' he shouted. Then, he too turned and swinging his staff, headed west.

Major Geraint Carlton cursed aloud, then immediately regretted it as his breath misted the visor of his respirator mask. He stopped, temporarily blinded by the fog, golden rule number one overlooked.

Golden rule number two was don't try to scratch the itch inside a frog suit. One always started as soon as the layers of material were pulled on and the rubber gloves snapped closed. He smiled, remembering rule number three – don't fart!

The major decided to use the enforced delay to do a further check on the readings. The counter crackled as he flicked the knobs. The needle settled: 150 Rads. Gamma; change range for airborne – 50 Sieverts. Hell! Levels this high after seven years? Definitely no scratching, Carlton my boy. One tear in this suit and you're history.

Make a note of location – Amber 25, formally Bodedern, B5109 roadway, 1500hrs. 03/06/2020. Time to move, ETA 1630hrs.

The soldier did a quick calculation and was confident he would complete the mission and be in good time for the drone helicopter rendezvous at 1800hrs. He stepped out briskly for the last leg of the journey. No vehicles, Command had said, stir up too much plute. Easier to decontaminate one man and, it occurred to Carlton to add, only one to lose if it goes wrong.

To break the tedium of the sweaty, lonely march, he went over in his mind the briefing details of yesterday:

'Island evacuated September 2013 following huge release fission products. Nuclear accident – commercial Magnox power plant. North coast Anglesey. Civilian casualties to date: 2,500. Military casualities: 52.'

Keep your wits about you, thought the young major. Let's not make it 53.

He remembered the press coverage of the disaster – an old reactor, bodged up repairs to some cracked welds. Commercial and political pressure to operate at maximum output, then a gas pipe ruptures. Panic and poorly trained staff make the situation worse. 500 tonnes of radioactive rubbish spews out.

They were lucky to contain it. Lucky it happened on an island. Blow up the bridges, no over-flying, no boats. Just make the place a prison, not for keeping people in but to keep them out. Now, not a living soul, not a cat or dog, not even a mouse – they were either shot or the radiation did for them. The colonel who gave the orders said it would be at least a hundred years before they considered a clean up, let alone repopulation.

Carlton thought again about the reason he was here. It seemed bizarre, impossible but it had to be checked out.

The old man leaned heavily on his staff. His heart was as weary as his legs and it had been a tiring walk. The strangeness of it all – the stone buildings and solid, black pathways, metal carts – all abandoned. No people, no horses, not even a bird.

'I heard him call my name and I knew I must come. Clearly, I heard it across the centuries. The land has died.'

His friend soothed him. 'Perhaps it was meant to be. A warning? But why are we called here? What can we do?'

'Look, here are the saplings we planted, full grown, and others beside.'

It was then that they heard their Master's instructions. Seiriol and Cybi wept.

Major Carlton finally cut his way through the overgrown hedge and double-checked his Satscan co-ordinates. This was definitely the correct location. The orbiting satellite had detected life forms in this restricted area. They had been evident for some days. His job – the mission – was to investigate and, if confirmed, to eliminate. All evidence to be destroyed.

A detailed search indicated some activity which must be human. Some husks of fresh bread lay on a slab, two young saplings, Yew he thought, had recently been planted. No footprints though, curiously the ground had not been disturbed. As a matter of routine he checked for radiation.

Carlton checked, swore, then checked again. No, he was right – no reading. The place was absolutely clear. Twiddle the knobs as he may, increase sensitivity – still no reading. It was incredibly clean, as if it had always been so. He punched out his report on the keypad, knowing that it made no sense. Assuming it would not be believed, he concluded with, 'location Red 12, formally Llanddeusant (Church of the Two Saints)'.

After an hour, Carlton had his reply:

'Message received Zulu Victor 73. Confirm analysis – your ingested alpha particles terminal. Medivac untenable deepest regret. Dependent alleviation activated. Mission success, congratulations. C in C. Ends.'

He snapped closed his transceiver and gave a rueful grin as he tore off the face mask, a neat ending for all concerned. No one to tell and no one to listen to his weird story.

A hand alighted on his right shoulder, then another, on his left. Two figures stood beside him, robed in white, each carrying a wooden stave. A third voice from somewhere close by, spoke gently.

'Follow the two men, Geraint. They will lead you to your new home.'

THE CALL
by Geoffrey Lincoln

Last night, in sleep,
drifting through midnight woods,
opaque and enigmatic,
unexpectedly, in a moonlit clearing
I came upon a garden,
fragrant with summer blossom.

Brambles, serpent-like,
covered the path behind me;
and even as I gazed
upon this bright retreat,
so lovingly tended
by ghosts of long departed hands,
I sensed the transformation
as ivy stealthily replaced
her sombre counterpane
until a favoured visitor
should pass that way again.

In the gloom beyond,
austere, decaying,
the old house watched.
Did I hear a whispered 'Come!'

and close behind,
the faintest echo
of a child's laughter?

Quietly the door unlatched,
revealing, in melancholy silence,
an empty corridor.
No pageant of former glory here,
only a gracious welcome
for a guest, long absent.

Cobwebs adorned the walls,
shrouding shadowed rooms
that patiently anticipated
my long awaited coming;
shyly inviting me to resurrect
deep-buried memories.

And there, in a corner,
dust-covered and forlorn,
lit by a fragile moonbeam
that struggled through
the clouded glass of a high window –
just a trifle,
a mere forgotten fragment:

a small black woollen glove.

IN PRAISE OF SEAWEED
by Val Owen

Seaweed, terrible stuff, just makes the rocks slippery, litters the beach, gets in the way of swimmers and clogs up boat propellers! But let me take you for a closer look at this 'weed' and its varieties.

First there are the brown wracks on the rocks between the high and low watermarks. Examine them closely and you will see they are not all the same. Hold up a piece which grows at the top of the rocks and see how it twists round, hence the name spiral wrack. Next down the rocks there is the bladder wrack. That is the one with the gas bladders along the frond. Have you tried popping these miniature balloons? They are tough and rubbery.

Follow the tide out further to the toothed wrack which does not have gas bladders but has tooth-like serrations along the edge of the frond. Now wait for the lowest waters of the spring tides (these are the tides which happen at the time of the spring and autumn equinox). You can find the edge of the kelp-bed. The kelps are the largest seaweeds around the coast of Anglesey and can grow up to four metres long. They form the forests of the seabed with their stems and long flattened blades which float back and forth with the currents in the water.

Now you have got your eye in, let's look for some of the smaller seaweeds. There are the delicate green varieties such as

the sea lettuce which is like crumpled membranes. Another group of seaweed or algae, to give the scientific name, are the reds. Many of these are quite small and have a dark red colour. You may find them attached to other seaweeds or in rock pools.

Seaweeds are true plants and contain green chlorophyll which enables them to absorb light to synthesis sugars. However, they form a group of plants which has adapted to a challenging environment. Those growing between high and low water have two periods in every twenty-four hours when they are under the swirling sea with the constantly changing direction of flow. They need the ability to flex with the current. I mentioned the tough rubbery texture of the gas bladders: it is this texture of the plant which enables it to bend without snapping. Seaweeds do not need roots as they are surrounded by water providing the essential minerals which are drawn up through the roots of a land plant. However, there is a need to hold tight to the rocks to avoid being swept away so they have a root-like structure, the holdfast, which does just that and anchors the plant in surging tides and storm waves. When the tide goes out, the environ-ment changes completely. They are exposed to direct baking sunlight while encrusted with a layer of salt left as the seawater evaporates, perfect drying conditions! The plants must withstand this period of dehydration. The jelly-like content of the seaweeds is partly responsible for this ability to withstand desiccation. And while we talk about jelly...

Does seaweed have any uses other than offering shelter and hiding places for a myriad of small fish, shrimps, sea urchins, small crabs, limpets, periwinkles and other sea creatures?

Yes, algae can be boiled down to extract the jelly which is the agar jelly used in laboratories to grow bacteria. It is also a food constituent and a component of cosmetics.

Round the world numerous seaweeds are eaten. There is lava bread in Wales, which is made from Purple Laver, a red seaweed. The wrap which goes round the rice of Japanese sushi is made of a seaweed called nori which is similar to lava bread.

Seaweeds are rich in vitamins B and C, and are an excellent source of trace minerals. Cattle and sheep graze the weed-covered shores of some islands, while coastal communities have used the weeds as a fertilizer to enhance the quality of poor stony soil. Seaweed products are used as food additives in animal and pet food.

Global warming, due to the emission of greenhouse gases, is a problem which might be partly solved by seaweed, it has been suggested. Algae absorb carbon dioxide so there has been a proposal that huge beds of seaweed could be grown and then harvested to use as a fuel.

So next time you slip on a smelly bit of weed on the beach remember that these of plants are great survivors, that it may be used in the seaweed wrap of your next beauty spa treatment, be part of your or your pets' diet and may help save the world from global warming.

WHERE ARE YOU NOW?
by Carole Albrecht

Oh where can I find you now?
I left you in Llanbadrig and there is so much to tell since then,
so much to share.
Can you hear the news where you are now?

Did you know that Jo has left Sarah?
That Dick has a baby girl and Sally is expecting twins?
Did you know that Sean has a different job,
that Clare is not very happy?
You would worry for them.
P and P are soldiering on so nothing much changes there.
Alice keeps going but her guy has gone.
Did you know?

There is so much to tell,
so much to share
but can you hear the news?
Can you feel the sun?
Hear the grass growing?
Hear the rain, the wind, the waves crashing?
Oh where are you now?

OLD BONES
by Georgina Parker

There was a loud 'plop' and the circle of ripples enlarged. Huw Jones cursed softly under his breath at the elusive fish. It was a late September evening and the Menai Straits were tranquil. The sun had disappeared but the afterglow still tinted the distant mountains and the edges of the layered clouds. Not a soul stirred along the shore.

Huw was sad and worried. He had lived in the nearby village all his seventy six years and had fished here many times, catching many fish. This evening he hadn't had a bite and his reflection in the glassy water troubled him.

He was a slight, gnarled man with grey stubbly cheeks and scalp. In his jeans and customary cap, he looked an elfish figure, especially when he chuckled and his monkey-like face creased up into a grin. These days Huw moved slowly and his rheumatic pain made him a frequent visitor to the local hospital.

He cursed again, dismissing his thoughts of ill-health, and whistled softly. A pale shape emerged from the trees about fifty yards down the shore. A young greyhound gracefully crossed the pebbly beach towards him. Huw's face lit up, as it always did when he saw his dog, and he put out a hand to pat her.

'Come on girl, let's go home,' he said in Welsh, and pulled in his line for the last time.

They set off along the shore, Ginny running ahead, while

Huw toiled behind, an anxious figure in the twilight. As he rounded the curve, he saw Ginny up against the base of a red cliff. She was digging and scratching at something in the shingle. When Huw approached he could make out a shadowy shape perhaps three feet long, and, assuming it to be a piece of driftwood, he called the dog. Ginny, however, was absorbed in her game and would not come. In exasperation Huw came closer, and then stopped abruptly.

Sticking out of the shingle was a long, greyish tusk! 'Yes, tusk', thought Huw, turning over the unfamiliar English word in his mind. Undoubtedly it was a tusk and Ginny had unearthed the bony part of the head to which it was attached. Huw could see part of the eye- socket but the rest lay buried.

He ran his hand gingerly down the smooth tusk and thought. The only thing he could remember from his brief education was a picture book showing great mammoths from the past. The ground around looked recently disturbed and he wondered if the gale the previous weekend could have unearthed the object? He glanced at the darkening sky, shivered away his disturbing thoughts and called Ginny, who had lost interest in her discovery.

Better go home and tell them what he had found. Would they believe him? It was a very strange fishing story...

The plump man in the brown raincoat was getting impatient. That wretched woman had been in the phone box for ages and he had a very important call to make. Important and exciting! He shrugged off the shadow of anxiety he felt about phoning the great Dr Shankley. Of course, Dr Shankley, the President of his local Antiquarian Society would be pleased. Perhaps he would even come to Anglesey to examine the find himself? Arthur Soames, keen amateur palaeontologist, was convinced his 'find' merited such attention.

It was pure chance that he had even heard about it. Mrs. Hughes, Argraig, with whom he and his family were staying for a fortnight's B&B had mentioned it in passing at breakfast, having heard about it from her friend, Bethan Morris.

According to Bethan, some old man from the village had been walking along the shore late at night and had been frightened out of his wits by the sight of two gleaming tusks. They were standing up on the pebbly beach fully six foot high like an ill-omen! Not just that, there was a head attached too, a huge skull! Heavens knows what else might be buried there. Of course the fanciful Bethan might have exaggerated but half the village was talking about it.

Arthur was extremely interested and intent on investigating. He had donned, what his patient wife called his 'fossil-grubbing gear', and headed for the Menai shore immediately. All the way back to the village he had imagined himself lecturing on pre-historic mammals to the Royal Society – hence the urgent phone call.

During the next six days, amazed locals lost count of the strange faces in the village and the spate of cars heading for the narrow track to the shore. Curious holiday-makers came from all over the island to watch distinguished scientists and enthusiastic amateurs working on 'the site'. Members of the Press quizzed locals, photographers shot film, and articles ran in the *Daily Post*. Even more exciting was the arrival of a BBC Wales film crew, striding about the village and the sea shore.

By Thursday evening the bones of some huge mammal had been extracted from the foreshore, neatly labelled in long rows, and carefully packed and loaded onto a large lorry for delivery to a specialised, academic establishment, deep in Wales. The scholars produced their books, theories and diagrams, and the long debate began.

The bar of the local pub was packed on Saturday night. Local lads in their Saturday night gear, holiday-makers in unseasonable beach clothes, villagers looking for a quiet night out and a sprinkling of professional men in suits and dark ties. In one corner of the noisy bar Huw, and his mate Evan, sat watching the crowd and slowly sipping their pints.

'Crowded tonight,' remarked Evan, 'it's still that fuss about the thing on the shore I expect.'

'I can't help wondering if I did the right thing by telling Maggi Hirael about it,' murmured Huw.

Evan's face was thoughtful. 'If you hadn't, someone else would', was his practical reply. 'Besides, hasn't done local trade any harm has it?' Evan's daughter kept a guest house on the road to the shore. 'Them boffins can't decide what it is but I know. You wouldn't think an old bloke like me could tell those professors but I could!' He grinned. 'I know what it is alright.'

Huw looked at his friend in disbelief and for a moment Evan looked annoyed. Then, lowering his voice he said, 'I remembered, this morning, when I read that bit in the paper about the pre-historic dinosaurs in North Wales.' He brought out the words slowly, lowering his voice still more, so that Huw had to bend forward to catch his words. 'It's an elephant Huw. I know it is!'

Huw thought his mate was pulling his leg. 'How would you know that?'

'Well,' Evan looked stealthily around the crowded pub, 'I vaguely remember a story I was told by me taid, when I was a lad. It was about a big circus coming to the island long ago. I know that because the bridge had just been built and me taid worked on the bridge. The circus was something special and it even had elephants. After going to Holyhead and Llangefni, it came to Newborough and pitched the big tent for the show. Somehow, that night, an elephant got loose and ran off. It caused quite a scare because people didn't know much about elephants then. Anyway, they eventually found it dead on the shore days later. No idea how it had got there without being seen, or why it had died. It was too big to move so they just dug a deep hole all around it and buried it. Me taid helped to get ropes from the construction site at the bridge to lend to the circus people. That's all I know, but I reckon I'm one of the few who knows that.' Evan grinned, 'But that's more than they do!' He pointed at the animated faces above the professional suits.

'Ought we to tell them?' Huw asked, his face a study.

Evan laughed. 'No. I dare say it won't be long before someone else remembers the elephant. Besides, we old folk don't get many thanks for correcting our youngers and betters today, do we?' He winked at Huw. 'Let them puzzle a bit longer shall we?'

Huw nodded. The two old friends smiled at each other through the smoke, with the childish delight of a shared secret and toasted the elephant of the Menai Straits with another couple of pints of bitter.

PICNIC ON LLANDDWYN ISLAND

by E Jones

Hey! You fair weather picnickers,
pack up and move away!
It's easy being adventurous
on a warm and sunny day,
and having a meal al fresco
when the weather's nice and hot.
You and your designer hamper!
You're sitting in my spot!
Even in winter I sit there
looking at that perfect view.
I brave all kinds of weather
with my flask of tasty stew.

You don't know the ways of the sea,
on that I'll lay a bet
You haven't watched how the tide comes in
and soon you'll all get wet!

PRINCESS JOAN
by Ross Davies

L lanfaes, close to the town of Beaumaris on Anglesey, has always been a place of great historical interest. This small hamlet, which lies close to the entrance of the Menai Straits, has a history that dates back to ancient times but this particular story comes from the 12th century and concerns a Welsh Princess.

The story starts with Prince Llewelyn I (Llewelyn the Great) Prince of Gwynedd, who was born at Nant Conwy in 1173. As the firstborn son of royal parents, he was fostered out at a very early age to a family in Powys. This was according to ancient Celtic custom, possibly to protect the young heir from malicious harm. The foster family lived close to the border between England and Wales so the young prince grew up in an atmosphere where skirmishes and battles were constantly fought. He learned a great deal about the ways and customs of the English and even their language. By the time he was 14 years old he was already a seasoned warrior.

The King of England at that time was Richard I (Richard Lion Heart) but, of the ten years of his reign, Richard only spent ten months in England. For the remainder of the time he was in the Middle East fighting in the Crusades. In his absence, his brother John ruled England as regent. On Richard's death in 1199, John became king in his own right.

In the meantime, on the Welsh side of the border, Llewelyn

had been busy reclaiming Gwynedd, piece by piece until, in 1201 at the age of 28, he was declared Lord of all Gwynedd and all the land north of Conwy – Perfeddwlad – reaching to the English border.

His increasing power did not please King John, who had been keeping a very wary eye on Wales but being a wily and devious man, he decided to try a different tack with the young and ambitious prince. He met Llewelyn in an attempt to persuade him to sign a treaty of 'Loyalty to the Crown', by offering to publicly state that Llewelyn be declared the true prince of all the land that he had recently acquired.

Llewelyn was too shrewd a man to refuse such an offer. He knew only too well that the time was not ripe for a military stand against the English. He signed the treaty. Three years later, in a bid to retain that loyalty, John offered him his natural daughter Joan in marriage, together with the castle, manor and land of Ellesmere as a dowry. Now Llewelyn had land in England.

Joan was the outcome of a liaison between John and one of the ladies-in-waiting at the English court. She was barely of marriageable age and about to become the wife of a man at least 16 years her senior and become a princess in a strange land. A girl, no more than thirteen years of age, who had been reared in the sophisticated atmosphere of a Norman English court.

However, Joan faced up to her duties with remarkable courage and eventually earned the respect of the Welsh people. They had been suspicious of her in the beginning because of her English bloodline. The Princess soon proved herself invaluable, both as a wife to Llewelyn and as a partner in his dealings with her father. She was used as a mediator and an envoy whenever possible. King John, despite his reputation for fickle behaviour, seemed always ready to listen to her views. Over the years, she and Llewelyn had five children, a son David and four daughters, but there is a bitter twist to the story.

Llewelyn had gone to South Wales to fight against the continuing English incursions across the border. He captured a Marcher Lord called William de Breos and sent him to be imprisoned at his palace at Abergwyngregyn in North Wales. Llewelyn was well aware of this man's importance so he allowed him limited liberty under the watchful eye and supervision of Princess Joan.

Knowing that de Breos had a son of marriageable age, Llewelyn was hopeful of a marriage settlement with his eldest daughter. Unfortunately, William de Breos was something of a womaniser and he made a play for Princess Joan. Although many years older than him, she fell hopelessly in love and their affair became so obvious that Llewelyn was informed. He hurried back home, a devastated man, and immediately had Joan imprisoned. A few days later, de Breos was publicly hanged in full view, as the story goes, of the tower where Joan was imprisoned. It was a very dangerous action for Llewelyn to take against such a powerful Marcher Lord.

Amazingly, no retribution came. The de Breos family seemed to have accepted that William had acted dishonourably. No reproach came from the English crown either. By now, King John had died and his young son, Henry III was on the throne. Quiet negotiations took place between Llewelyn and the new English King and by 1232, Joan was back by her husband's side.

The truth was that he loved her and could not do without her help as a wife or as his trusted counsellor in diplomatic matters.

Joan died five years later in 1237 and it is proof of Llewelyn's deep feelings for her that he honoured her final wishes. She had often gazed across the sea from Abergwyngregyn to the Island of Anglesey and told him of her wish to be buried there. He had founded a friary at Llanfaes, some years before and he arranged for her body to be carried over the Levan sands and be buried in the grounds. Llewelyn died in 1240, at the age of 67 and was buried at Nant Conwy.

Sometime during the 1930s, a group of archaeologists were surveying the area at Llanfaes when they came across a water trough made of stone, used by cattle in a field. The lid lay nearby. Upon examination they were astounded to find that it was the stone coffin of Princess Joan and that her effigy was on the lid. Today, it is on display at the church of St Nicholas and St Mary at Beaumaris.

MOELFRE LIFEBOAT DAY

by Joy Mawby

Isobel, Simon and Joy
with bulging holiday purses.
Three shining, expectant faces,
sun-touched and rosy.

Sea-mixed music and voices
meet them across the bay,
fluttering stalls and bunting.
Going to Lifeboat day.

Clamour of people and laughter.
Hoopla – Simon's won
Brut aftershave for Daddy
and lollies for everyone.
Joy's trying to find the treasure,
she digs up fifty pence.
'I'll lose if I have another go.'
Joy – full of common sense.
Isobel fishes the crab out
and is handed back her money,
buys shell encrusted wooden box
'Purple – just right for Mummy.'

Now, salt wind blusters and billows
scrumptious wafts from a big white van.
Crispy chips fly from plates like rockets.

Catch them if you can!
They sit in a real live lifeboat,
eyes big at the tales of the sea.
They wish they were storm-tossed on oceans
instead of tied up at the quay!
Failing that, there is the roundabout,
they're strapped in and holding tight.
'Make it go faster and faster!'
They shout in fearful delight.
All's spinning, colours mixing,
music's roaring, tummy's turning –
Wow!

Isobel, Simon and Joy
with empty holiday purses.
Three smiling, exultant faces,
sun-touched and rosy.

They hug precious prizes,
walk slowly away –
all wrapped in the magic
of Lifeboat Day.

CEILIOG

gan Gwyn M Lloyd

Ganwaith bu deffro'n gynnar – i dwrw
Y deryn â'i glochdar.
O Dduw, pam ar y ddaear
Wnest ti hwn pan wnest ti iâr?

A PLACE FOR ANGELS
by Kim Jones

'I sn't that just a little bit bland?' remarked the Fallen Angel. 'It could do with livening up.'

God pressed control/save then swivelled his chair round to face his assistant. 'Did I ask for your opinion?'

'No, but it stands to reason, if you're going to give mankind intelligence he's going to need some kind of challenge. Life could get very boring surrounded by so much virtue.'

'You don't know what you're talking about, as usual.' God leaned back in his leather director's chair and put his feet on the desk. 'I am creating a perfect world. It's so close to Paradise, it ticks all the boxes.'

'You don't get it, do you?' The Fallen Angel was on his soapbox again, God recognised the signs. 'If you're going to give mankind the freedom of choice he's got to have something to choose between. He needs alternatives.'

'Like right and wrong, good and evil, salad or fry-up?'

'Exactly. If you don't give him an alternative to every virtue he'll only start making them up himself and God knows where that'll lead.'

'But I don't.'

'True.' The Fallen Angel opened his laptop. 'I'd better start making a list of possible alternative virtues.'

'Do we need one for each of them?'

'Shouldn't think so. Half a dozen should do, as long as they're deadly enough.'

'The half-a-dozen deadly alternative virtues ...' mused God. 'Doesn't exactly roll off the tongue does it?'

The Fallen Angel clicked onto Thesaurus. 'We could call them vices, that's less of a mouthful. Or, what about 'sins'?'

'Yes!' said God, sitting up straight and putting his feet back on the floor with an almighty thump. 'Sins! I like it. The half-a-dozen deadly sins. What shall we say they are?'

'I suppose one could say 'pride',' suggested the Fallen Angel with a hint of self-satisfaction.

'Covetousness,' said God, thinking that if he weren't careful his assistant would be taking over the entire project.

The Fallen Angel walked over to God's consul and placed a claw-like finger on the mouse. A mottled blue and green globe surrounded by a border of fluffy pink clouds floated onto the screen.

'Is that it?'

'Yes. That's the world. What do you think?'

'Wicked!' The Fallen Angel leaned closer, his fiery breath clouding the screen. 'But there's an awful lot of blue.'

'That's water. And the green bits are where mankind is going to live. You see, I'm creating several different species and I thought that if I surrounded each piece of land with plenty of water, call it an ocean for example, it would stop any... It would keep them ...'

'More eco-friendly than a high wire fence, I suppose. Are you planning to keep mankind on one side of the planet and womankind on the other?'

'Womankind? Ah yes, I'd forgotten about the spare rib. No, no, that wouldn't work at all. The way I see it, they've got to be mixed together in order to ... you know.'

'In that case you'd better add 'lust' to your list.'

God banged his mouse down on the desk. 'What's wrong with you? You always look at the worst case scenario!'

'Now, now ... temper, temper!' The Fallen Angel picked up his broken halo and made for the door. 'I'm going for a coffee. D'you want anything from the canteen?'

God twanged the celestial harp on his screen-saver. 'A Danish would be nice.' He fumbled for some change. 'Make that two.'

'Thanks, but I'm on a diet.'

'They're both for me,' and with a repentant sigh, God added 'gluttony' to his list.

'I can't decide between 'envy' and 'sloth' for the final sin,' declared the Fallen Angel, sipping his latte.

'I suppose we could use them both.' God was feeling benevolent after two Pecan-butter Danish pastries and regretted his earlier tantrum.

'The half-a-dozen plus one deadly sin,' murmured the Fallen Angel. It's not exactly the best household slogan I've ever heard. A bit too much like 'have six get one free'. It's going to need a bit of work but it's not as if it's set in tablets of stone, is it?'

'Why not simply 'The Seven Deadly Sins'?'

'No. Much too straightforward. No-one's going to remember that phrase.'

But God was getting bored with all this talk of sin and vice. He began doodling on the map of the world, dragons and serpents appeared in the margins.

'What is that arrow pointing at?' the Fallen Angel could see he'd lost God's attention.

'That arrow? Oh, that's where I thought I'd put the Garden of Eden.'

'You're building gardens already?'

'Yes, the Garden of Eden. It's going to be an earthly sort of Paradise.'

'For mankind to live in?'

'Actually, I was thinking more of buying a Holiday Cottage there.'

'Oh good! Can I come and stay?'

'No. The whole point about the Garden of Eden is that only good things will be allowed in.'

'And you're going to put people there!'

'Maybe a few angels, for company. It'll be somewhere for me to chill.'

'Chill? It doesn't sound like my kind of place, at all.'

'No. It won't be your climate of preference.'

'Not my kind of company either. But – T.H.E.G.A.R.D.E.N. O.F.E.D.E.N. – it's a lot of letters to get into such a small space. Perhaps you should shorten it,' the F.A. suggested.

'You're right,' G. agreed. 'If it's to be a place for angels shall I just call it Anglesey?'

THE MAIL BOAT
by Owen Charles Parry-Jones

Railways and ships have vapours
Of the night train newspapers,
Steam gone,
Fish-clear cold faced air
Freshens my moist eyes,
Which stare,
Into the dark at the rail
For the slow shape of the mail.
The station fills her stable,
Two ships linked by a cable,
Their bows
From the dock climbing,
Limpid green water lapping,
Hibernia and Cambria,
They were never in closer,
As in Holyhead harbour
In love at the midnight hour.

FOUR GLASSES
AND A BAPTISM
by David Crystal

I was in the small town of Uherske Hradiste, in the south-east of the Czech Republic, as part of its British film festival. My role was to introduce a series of British films and to give a couple of talks on language in relation to the task of adaptation from book to film. They were showing Roman Polanski's *Tess*, which brilliantly adapted the Wessex dialect of Thomas Hardy, and Ang Lee's *Sense and Sensibility*, which replaced Jane Austen's complex and mannered sentences by a modern-sounding elliptical dialogue.

It was an enthralling event. The town was packed with enthusiasts from all over Europe. Films were being shown in local halls and on a huge screen in the town square – the weather was on the film-goers side – as well as in the main cinema.

It was the cinema's fortieth birthday, and an illustrated memorial book had been published to mark the occasion. Along with the festival director and the sponsors, I was invited to be a godfather for the book. A godfather for a book? I thought I'd misheard, so I asked for a repeat of the question. No, I'd heard correctly. A godfather.

It's an intriguing idea, and – as I later discovered – quite an old one. In the dedication to his first major poem, *Venus and Adonis*, Shakespeare refers to the Earl of Southampton as being the poem's godfather. And in 1737, Henry Fielding wrote in the Preface to his play, *The Historical Register of the Year 1736*, that his bookseller thought a patron was 'a kind of God-father to a Book, and a good Author ought as carefully to provide a Patron to his Works, as a good Parent should a God-father to his Children'.

I know what's involved in being a godfather, as I've been one several times. Attend baptism. Adopt suitably pseudo-paternal expression. Say prayers with parents on behalf of child. Watch while water poured gently over back of child's head. Go 'Awww' when child cries. Give present. Retire to house for celebratory eats, and, if lucky, celebratory champagne. Drink toast to child.

But what does one do for a book? There could hardly be a baptism for an inanimate object. I waited uncertainly at the front of the packed cinema, along with my co-sponsors. A copy of the book was brought in, resting on a tray. On top of the book were four glasses of white wine. Huge applause and cheers.

When everyone had quietened down, the director said a few words about the cinema, the festival, and the anniversary. Then he turned to us and invited us to raise our glasses. I was beginning to feel anticipatorily merry. My taste-buds were tingling. I waited, ready to follow his lead. He turned towards the book, bowed, and then ...

... poured the wine slowly over the book, and invited us to do the same.

One by one, we did just that. I was the last. The others took good care to make sure that the whole of the book was given a good wetting. So I did too. The top part of the spine seemed a little dry. I dealt with it professionally.

I have never deliberately poured wine, or any liquid, over a book before. Inadvertently, maybe. But here it was, now resting happily on a tray with the wine lapping lazily around its pages. It seemed very happy. As was everyone else in the cinema.

I must say I found the experience curiously moving. Godfather of a book, eh? I wondered about the future well-being of my new goddaughter. (The word for book in Czech is *kniha*, a feminine noun, so I assumed it was female.) 'What are my responsibilities towards this book?', I asked them. Tell the world about it, they said.

So now I do.

CYDRADDOLDEB HILIOL
gan Alan Wyn Roberts

Cyfartal ydynt a'r ddau mewn cymod
Yn un a chytun yn lliw eu cysgod.

FOR THE LOVE
OF LLANDDWYN
by Carol Mead

I take a path where pilgrims walked before
And think of wishes made from hearts entwined
I follow fingers pointing to the sea
And touch the grasses strewn amongst the dunes
They sigh and whisper, *'Dwynwen'*

Within the blue I watch the seabirds soar
And on my lips a splash of ocean spray
I taste the salty bitterness of loss
A ruined church, a wishing well, a cross
They hold the prayers of, *'Dwynwen'*

Here in a valley pilots lived to save
'Twr Mawr' was built to guide them on their way
From out of Valley rookies learn to fly
I watch them trailing letters in the sky
They stir the word, *'Dwynwen'*

Then on a pillowed rock I lay my head
To listen to the sounds around me now
Jets, a barking dog, a laughing child
As to the west I watch the setting sun
But on the breeze – a curious cry … *'Maelon'*
'Maelon'

THE MOON AND THE STARS ARE ON SHOW

by Brian Stevens

We moved for a peaceful and pleasant retirement to the Isle of Anglesey. Since Manchester was not peaceful or pleasant there was nothing to keep us there. Let me explain.

I'm driving around a very troublesome estate – roughest area you'll find in rain-soaked Manchester. I am self employed, selling fresh tea cakes. They are still hot when I load my van at the bakery at 5.30 am. I have finished all the town shops by 7.00 am, beating the early morning rush hour. Heading into the estate on the outskirts of the city, I am about to get out of the van at 'Mike's' when a figure appears at the nearside window. He waves a gun with a silencer on it, demanding to be let in. I slip the locks and in he jumps. His gun points directly at me and he says in a menacing way, 'Drop me near Victoria Station.' I hear the gun click as a bullet drops into the firing position. I feel panic in my stomach. There's no sense in arguing. He holds all the aces.

'OK, the station it is,' I say. All the time, I'm aware of the gun. I know he can choose life or death for me and I also know which one he'll go for if I don't do as he says. I turn the motor round and head for the city. I keep my foot down, hoping we might get stopped by the law for speeding, but no such luck. He is on to me and jams the deadly weapon into my ribs.

'I know what your game is so slow down or I'll put a hole in your side.' With these words ringing in my ears, I quickly resort to a snail's pace. He laughs.

'This'll do me,' he says, pointing ahead. 'Drop me there.' The revolver disappears from view as the early morning criminal climbs out of the van.

This is one example of how our lives had become affected by crime. My wife had her handbag snatched by a fleet-footed youth. Our house was burgled by a night thief who added insult to crime by loading our car with everything he had stolen and then driving away. Then there were the dodgy bank machines, modified to regurgitate money not to us but to somebody else's eager hands.

Many cities suffer in the same way. Is it the economic climate? Is it the druggies desperate to feed the habit? All this crossed my mind as I drove home. Then I had a flash of inspiration – a thought that just wouldn't go away.

'We must move – move far away from here.' But where could we go?

Then it hit me. 'Anglesey. We'll go to Anglesey.' I could see in my mind's eye, that small island surrounded by blue water. I could see the beautiful beaches, golden sand and, out to sea, the dolphins performing their acrobatics in unison as if to say, 'We're here and here we are staying.'

We found a nice spot in which to settle, just a mile from the seaside town of Cemaes, which has an unspoilt beach. Our house had a spectacular sea view. If we needed convincing that we'd made the right move, it came the next day from our son's question, 'Will we be able to see the stars from here?' I thought of the factories we'd left behind, the ones which pumped out their acrid smoke, creating a blanket across the sky through which we could see nothing.

'Yes son, the stars will be on show every night.'

Years later, ill health dictated a change of transport for me. I became the proud owner of a disability 'scooter scrambler'. One day when the sun was cracking the flagstones, I parked it at our local milk bar to buy a refreshing cold drink. I sat drinking it at one of the tables outside in the glorious sunshine. This was paradise.

I was suddenly aware that coming my way was 'The Wild Bunch'. There were ten to twelve teenagers all on racing bikes and obviously intent on stopping at my place of rest. Forgetting where I was, for a moment, I braced myself for some abuse as they sat around me, but no. Their spokesman, pointing at my scrambler, politely asked me, 'Any chance we can have a go on that please?' Before I could answer the smallest of the group burped long and loud, perhaps as a protest against such politeness. The leader slapped him round the head adding, 'Watch your manners.' I liked him and his friends so I decided to let them all have a go on the scrambler, down to the park and back, even the smallest – the rebel without a cause.

'I must get home now,' I said as the last one returned. I climbed on to my trusty steed and said, 'Goodbye' to a rousing back slapping routine. They were well pleased with me.

I hadn't gone far when the Wild Bunch joined me. They formed a guard of honour. Two rode in front of me, one rode each side and the rest followed behind in twos. 'How different from my encounters in Manchester,' I thought as we slowed to a halt outside my house.

'Thank you,' I called to them.

'It's a pleasure, mister,' said the leader solemnly. 'One good turn deserves another.' And with a swift about turn they rode away.

YNYS
by Annee Griffiths

Woman watches by the window
looking out to sea.
Down below,
waves crash against the rocks
on the island of storms.

Between the sea
and the window,
in tiny fields fenced
with stone and gorse,
black cows
follow their mouths,
like the woman
grazing her thoughts
on the island of storms.

Woman who watches
sits by the tiny window
shrunk into the deep recess
of the old white wall.
Beyond through fog
the lighthouse flashes
a path to the sea
horizons hedged by cloud
on the island of storms.

Woman watches by the window,
listens to her breath whistling softly,
like the wind in the cracks.
Wind wailing its soft duet
with seals on the shore.
Clock ticking
counts through centuries
of a woman watching by the window
on the island of storms.

FFENESTR BYWYD
gan J Richard Williams

Drwy wydr plaen y ffenestr gwyliai wyrth y Nef,
a gweld y machlud euraid
o'i flaen,
wnai ef.

Yn lliwiau'r haul auroren ar fynd i'w wely llaith,
cysidrai ef ei fuchedd
ar hyd
y daith.

O edrych allan drwyddi, fe welai eto'i rawd
yn blentyn, mab a phriod,
yn dad
a brawd.

Pe gallai edrych eilwaith a gweld o'r ochr draw
fe welai Duw yn aros,
i'w arwain,
law yn llaw.

Drych enaid yw y ffenestr yn dangos modd ein byw
a ddylai adlewyrchu'r patrwm
a roed
gan Dduw.

CAN YOU HEAR ME?
by June Roberts

C an you hear me? Come closer. Put your hand on the stone. Can you feel the warmth beneath the coolness? That's because I'm here.

Oh my bones have long since gone, but my heart is here. That's why you can understand me. Heart speaking to heart. My languages were Norman-French and Welsh, with a smattering of English, and yours ... it doesn't matter, because you understand me anyway. Make yourself comfortable. You just have to be near me to learn my story. That pew over there will do.

Mine is a love story. Does that shock you? No? Maybe it's different in your time, but in my time, the twelfth century, we women, especially aristocrats, were not expected to think about love. The church had problems with us anyway, because of Eve and that business in the Garden of Eden, and our lives were run by men: fathers, husbands and sons, and the demands of property.

There's not a lot you can do about human nature though. I was the result of a brief affair between Prince John and my mother, a minor noblewoman. When she found she was pregnant with me, he had moved on to someone else, and princes cannot marry where they choose. Her family banished her to live in a small cottage on distant lands of theirs with only a maid for company. She died when I was eight and my uncle sent me to John who was king by this time. You hear a lot of bad things about my father, but he was good to his natural children. He wanted a crown for me, his only natural daughter, and he found one of a kind.

I was fourteen when I was married to Llewellyn, Prince of Gwynedd. You know him as Llewellyn the Great. It was fortunate that the Welsh didn't recognise illegitimacy, so it wasn't a barrier to our marriage. It was a political arrangement of course. Llewellyn was twice my age, but I was to discover he was as handsome intelligent and kind, as he was brave and ruthless in battle.

So I came here to this foreign country, far away from my home and family. Although my husband and some of his nobles could speak French, most people spoke Welsh. It was difficult at first but I worked hard and learned to make the best of my position, and he made sure I was given the respect due to me. He knew that my way was going to be difficult. I was a hated foreigner, the daughter of bad King John, but I was strong, and I was young. I understood the ways of a court and quite a lot about politics. I was useful to my husband. I had children.

There were other women in my husband's life of course, as is the way with princes. He was often away for months on campaign. There had been relationships before me with women he could not marry. I understood this. I didn't like it but I understood it and he didn't flaunt these liaisons in front of me as Norman lords might have done. I knew now that I came first, that I was special to him. Imagine my anger, when I came home early from a visit and found that there was a woman in our bed.

I threw her out and had the bed and hangings taken out and burned in the courtyard.

I expected a beating for that. I was truly afraid, but I did not know then that I was quite within my rights under Welsh law. Even if I had killed the woman, I would not have been punished. It was even possible for a Welsh woman to divorce her husband after three occasions of adultery. It was possible to separate after seven years and retain half of the joint goods. Welsh law understood something about the human heart. My husband was philosophical, even a little admiring about what I had done. I seemed to go up in everyone's estimation after that.

But I was often lonely, and when Will de Breose, a Norman lord whom my husband had taken prisoner during one of his campaigns, started paying me attention, I tried hard to resist. He was charming, handsome and reminded me of home. Eventually, I succumbed. It was only the once, but Llewellyn returned home unexpectedly and found us. I will never forget his face. The pain and fury written there were indescribable.

I expected him to kill us both on the spot. He actually shook with rage. Will was taken out and hanged and I expected to follow him. However Llewellyn decided to banish me. I was placed under house arrest at Abergwyngregyn, with a servant or two and the occasional visit of a priest as my only relief from isolation. I was well guarded, allowed my books and embroidery and to walk a little. It seemed I was my mother's daughter after all. The wheel had turned full circle. I was beyond the pale, an object of disgust and disgrace. The months slipped by on slow footsteps and I began to know the full depths of loneliness and regret in that bitter isolation. I began to wish for death as my mother had done.

A year passed by. Then, one morning, when the sky was thick with showers and mist, I heard the thundering of many horses' hooves. The door burst open letting in the smack of wind and rain, and unbelievably, it was him. He pushed the maids outside, bellowed instructions that we were not be disturbed, grabbed me by the hair and took me there and then on the furs beside the fire and then again tenderly. In a storm of passion, tears and inarticulate endearments, we rediscovered and affirmed our love for each other.

Incredibly it seemed I was forgiven. I was to return as his princess, with all the deference that status commanded. Had such a thing ever happened in Christendom? I was so amazed that it quite took my breath away! He was placing his power in some jeopardy for me, for his people were angry with their foreign lady who had betrayed their beloved prince. But his word was law and they would obey him. It would be up to me to win back their respect. I looked at his face, marked with loss and pain with the rain still in his hair, and I knew I'd placed those marks there, and I vowed never to fail him again. And I never did.

I think he must have decided that there was a passionate Celtic streak in my nature, as there was in his and that helped to make his forgiveness possible. Never, by look, word or deed did he reproach me and we delighted in each other once again. And that delight lasted until death claimed us. In a way, it has never gone, not even now.

It warms my heart as I slumber, and I like to share its warmth.

He called me Siwan.

Are you glad you listened?

I wish you love.

I never expected to find it.

I hope you do.

Nothing can replace it.

BUZZARDS AT DIN LLIGWY

by Katherine Hutchings

The winds are wild where buzzards fly
Keen as a blade, sharp as the eye
That searches out these ancient stones
Embedded in the Island's bones
Where shadows die.

'Neath Lligwy's capstoned cromlech lie
The shades of ancients who passed by
This place, then stayed and made their homes
Where buzzards fly.

Spiralling thermals, now hovering high,
Outlined against the wind-torn sky
Above the paths that once were known
To Druid priest, peasant and crone.
Do they still hear that haunting cry?
Where buzzards fly.

GOING HOME
by Janet Pritchard

I'm going back to Holyhead for a visit.' These words caused such a fuss.

'Indeed you're not!' Caroline had said sharply.

'Don't be ridiculous!' Cameron had added in the same tone of voice as his sister.

Beth had sighed, knowing that this argument could go on for a long time. She had asked her three grown up children to visit that day so that she could inform them of her decision. All three of them had sat round the kitchen table, looking at her as if she was insane. She had anticipated their reaction and waited patiently for the storm to pass.

The twins continued to rant, 'You're just being selfish.' Cameron had glanced at his sister for support.

'Thinking of no-one but yourself! You should be here with us, not gallivanting up north and making us worry' finished Caroline.

Beth had smiled to herself; the twins were so predictable. She knew that their reaction was only through concern for her. Whilst they argued, she had made a cup of tea and caught Simon's eye, silently pleading for his intervention.

'I think Mum should go,' he had said in his usual quiet manner. He was so like his father.

That had taken the wind out of their sails and they had eventually, but reluctantly, agreed but only after Simon had said that he would drive the three hundred miles to Anglesey and stay there with their mother.

Two days later, she stood at the beginning of Holyhead breakwater where Simon had dropped her off. She had grown up in Holyhead and the breakwater had been a special place. A happy place.

'Do you remember where the smallest stone is?' she asked her husband and laughed as her hand stroked the little stone. She had no idea if this was the smallest stone built into the structure, it was something her father had told her when she was a little girl and she had told Joe when they had walked here hand in hand as sweethearts, and in turn, it had been passed on to their children.

Walking along slowly, a seagull called and she looked up to the sky, the wind caught her hair and her nostrils filled with the salty air. She felt more alive at this moment than she had done for a long, long time. Memories came flooding back; she remembered the little train that ran from the quarry and along the top road, carrying huge rocks to re-enforce the mighty structure. The evidence was still there in places. Some of the tracks still lay where the workers had laid them more than a century ago. She leaned on the wall for a moment and looked out to sea towards the Skerries, remembering the old mail boats, 'What were their names Joe? I can't quite recall.' She smiled as she heard him reply, 'The Cambria and the Hibernia'. Ah, yes, she remembered now.

Carrying on towards the end of the breakwater where the

square lighthouse stood, names of other ships, now long gone, popped into her mind the Slieve League, Slieve Donard and the Princess Maud. She remembered that on a clear summer's day, just before the sunset, you could see the Mountains of Mourne in Ireland, the Cumbrian hills and the Isle of Man. At the lighthouse she turned to Joe, 'This is where we kissed for the first time.' She could almost feel the years slipping away. She had been shy and that first kiss had been the most exciting, tender experience of her young life.

Tears filled her eyes as she strolled down the steps to the bottom road; she looked over towards Newry Beach and to where the lifeboat used to run down the slipway. She remembered the two maroons lighting up the sky, calling the crewmen to the rescue, the huge splash as the boat hit the water and the thoughts of the poor mariners in distress.

Strolling along, memories, long forgotten, flooded her mind. 'Do you remember the raft that we used to swim out to Joe?' she asked, 'I nearly drowned because it was so far from the shore but you saved me and we lay on that raft for hours because I was too scared to swim back. I almost burned to a crisp in the sun.' She laughed aloud. 'And jumping off the Mackenzie Pier but only when the tide was high because you didn't like heights. Oh, what a pair we were!'

Eventually she reached 'their seat.' All the exhilaration of earlier had gone and she sat down on the hard cold slab under the stone arch. This is where they had sheltered from a sudden storm and where he had surprised her by going down on one knee to propose to her. The tears fell unchecked 'I'm so very tired, and I miss you so much Joe'.

'I know my love,' she heard him say and felt his hand in hers.

'The cancer has spread and it won't be long now,' she said, 'that's why I had to come back.'

She felt him squeeze her hand. 'Don't be frightened my dear, I'll be waiting for you, and then we'll be together always.'

The words comforted her. She leaned back and closed her eyes; she sat there for a long time with the wind in her face. 'Hi Mum,' it was Simon, 'I've come to take you home now. Ready?'

She smiled at her youngest son as he helped her up; she leaned heavily on his arm as they walked slowly the rest of the way.

Simon caught the smile, 'Happy memories from when Dad was alive?' he asked

'Oh, yes,' she breathed and turned to look back.

She saw Joe wave from 'their seat' and heard him say, 'See you soon my darling Beth'.

She smiled up at her son, 'I have only happy memories of Holyhead'.

MY FATHER'S HANDS
by Angela Christensen

Hands, once harsh and forceful,
Strong and weathered from manual labour,
Coarse to the touch,
Sometimes to be feared,
Seemingly not made for tenderness or caress.

Now, with age, made soft and gentle.
Pallid skin, thin and fragile,
Bruising all too easily.

A constant tremor – witness of frailty and vulnerability.
Gestures hesitant and powerless.
Joints swollen, fingers crooked.
Yet tender, oh so tender.

These hands epitomise the passage of a man.
The journey we all will take.

101 YEARS OF STORIES
While living in a care home,
Joan Foster-Smith
recounted some stories of her long
life to her son.

It's strange what you remember, isn't it?
When my son Tony said to me, 'You've lived a long time, Mother; you must have so many memories. I'd like to write some of them down,' my mind went blank. There he sat with his pen and paper and I could only think of orchids – pink, purple and mottled orchids – in a greenhouse. A girl was standing on one side of me and a man on the other. 'I met Neville Chamberlain once,' I said 'at Dorothy Chamberlain's Christmas party. He had a big orchid collection.' Tony wrote that down and then the carer came in with my tablets and it was time for Tony to go.

'I'll be back tomorrow,' he said as he kissed me. He comes every day. I'm lucky. Some people don't get any visitors.

I lay in bed wondering what I could tell him tomorrow. I'd lived in Birmingham as a child. Our neighbours were The Rev'd and Mrs Henry Guest and family. They invited me to stay at their cottage, in Llaneilian, when I was 11. I loved it. We swam, sailed and hiked. I'd never been anywhere as beautiful as North Wales. The Guest boys camped in a bell tent on the headland and got up to all sorts of mischief. They played jokes on passers-by – like the bunch of flowers on a piece of string trick. At home, our two families played tennis together in the summer.

I must tell Tony about my work for the judge. When I was at secretarial college I decided to improve my shorthand by volunteering to work in the law courts. I was assigned to a judge, who smiled at me. 'How kind of you to offer help, my dear,' he said and he handed me his wig. 'This has split just here, do you see?' He gave me a needle and some thread and left me to what he obviously felt was women's work. Tony will like that story.

The next day I told Tony about my first proper job. It was at the BBC in Birmingham. My boss, the cheerful Percy Edgar, instigated *Children's Hour*. We laughed, one Christmas, when a woman, calling herself 'Mother Goose' sent rotund Edgar a sweater five sizes too small. Tony remembered listening to *Children's Hour*. He hadn't realised that it had all started in Birmingham, which had its own 'Uncle Pat' and an 'Auntie Vi' too – Violet Carson, later famous as Ena Sharples of *Coronation Street*.

Tony knows the story of how I met his father but I wanted to re-tell it, as much for myself as for him. In 1930, Foster, a handsome young engineer came to stay with the Guests. He was on leave from his post with the Para Electric Company in Brazil. When we were introduced we found we both loved tennis. He asked me where I liked to go on holiday and I said 'Anglesey is my favourite place.' He liked it too and it was special to him because, whenever he was on his way home from Brazil, the ships picked up pilots from Lynas Point.

'When I see the lighthouse and the North Wales coast, I know I'm almost home,' he said.

Rain ruled tennis out one Saturday. Your father came round and said 'Will you come out to lunch with me?' He took me to Stratford-on-Avon and proposed and I accepted. We were in love. I was very excited and before your father could ask my parents' permission, I confided in my mother. She was horrified and said it was far too quick. In the end, we promised we'd wait two years. Mother wept on my wedding day and gave me a return ticket in case I didn't like Brazil.

I did like Brazil. We were so happy and had a house overlooking the park. Next door was the American Embassy. We were sometimes invited there, and once we met Charles Lindberg.

Life was good – swimming, tennis by floodlight in the cool evenings, watching the fiestas and attending dinners on visiting ships. It all came to an end in 1935 when the company was nationalised.

Your father was 42 and reckoned he could retire on the pension of a thousand a year. We went to the Guests' cottage in Llaneilian to make plans for the future. The lady opposite, who lived in 'Orta' was putting up a 'For Sale' notice. Your father helped her and she said, 'Why don't you buy this house? Then you can stay on in Llaneilian.' So we did. My housekeeping was £2 a week. Sometimes the postman supplied rabbits to supplement meat from the butcher. Hilary was born in 1936 and I had my hands full but your father was never happy unless he was working. He helped wire Amlwch's Royal Cinema and then looked round for something else. He obtained the post of electrical engineer for a Gold Mine in Colombia. He went ahead to arrange accommodation.

Hilary and I had an exciting trip out. Because of the mountainous terrain, one leg of the journey, along the River Necchi, was by sea-plane. There was engine trouble and we made an emergency landing. Fortunately no-one was hurt but there wasn't much food aboard and the repair took some time. We were objects of great interest to the local Indians who took pity on us and cooked us omelettes over an open fire.

Considering the difficulties in transporting goods over the mountains, it's amazing what a community arose around the mines. There were bungalows, a hospital, bar, clubhouse, swimming pool and tennis courts. A ranch supplied meat and dairy products. You, of course, were born in 1939 and Patrick in 1942.

My granddaughter Sarah brought her young sons, Sam and Ben, in today. 'Tell us the pig story, please,' they said as soon as they'd kissed me.

'Again?' They nodded and Sarah laughed.

'When we lived in Colombia,' I said. 'Your granddad, Tony, was given a pig as a present. She lived at the end of our garden. She was very friendly and snorted 'good morning' when we took her breakfast. One day I thought it was quiet so I went into the garden to see what Tony was doing and what did I see?'

'He was riding his favourite pig!' shouted the boys. 'And after that he often rode it until ...' Ben trailed off.

'The pig changed into sausages,' finished Sam. There was a little silence then – 'Could you tell us about Uncle Hilary on the windowsill, please?'

'Well, your great grandfather and I were on a trip and were staying in a New York hotel.'

'You were on the 15th floor up,' said Ben.

'Yes. Hilary went into the bathroom to brush his teeth. He was a long time so I went in and he wasn't there. He'd crawled out on to the window sill. I was very frightened and I told him to come in at once but he wouldn't. Then your great grandfather had a brilliant idea. He telephoned the hotel reception and asked them to phone our room immediately. They did and Hilary edged his way back and I lifted him in. Why do you think he came back?'

'Because he loved answering the telephone!'

How well they knew the stories but they never got tired of hearing them.

When war broke out, the British citizens wanted to go home, I told Tony the next day. However, they received a letter from Anthony Eden, asking them to stay. Britain required 'our' gold to buy destroyers which were desperately needed. We got news via *Radio Newsreel* but we worried constantly about our families at home.

We didn't get back to England until 1947. It was a dismal, snowy winter with rationing and rail strikes. We found boarding schools for you three boys and we bought a house in Solihull. Your father worked for the Electricity Board and every year we went to Llaneilian for family holidays.'

'I've got happy memories of those,' Tony said.

'Well, you know the rest. When your father finally retired, we bought 'Trefor' in Bull Bay. The purchase was settled on a handshake over a butcher's counter. We had fourteen happy years there before your father died.

I was content, then, to move to Llaneilian with my little cat. You'll remember I started to drive again. My licence dated from 1930 but I didn't have to re-take my test. I had a few lessons, though. How I loved zooming into town in your father's Triumph 2000.'

When I think about it, I'm amazed that when I was born the Titanic was still in the shipyard, the Great War hadn't begun and wireless, television and passenger planes were just a dream.

It's wonderful the things you remember, isn't it – and weren't the days always sunny?

G.J.F-S. Dec 8th 1910 – May 20th 2012
R.I.P.

CAE CARREG CORN
for Paul Matthews
by Fiona Owen

What is it, wind-through-the-tall-grass?
You seem to have stopped me, here,
on the path (again) through the field;
you seem to be whispering in something
like a voice, which meets my own inwardness,
which says there is a lesson here for exactly
you among these stalks of grass, debris of the year's turning,
life-stuff gone dead.

Sighs spread rumours across the field
of shifts and subtle reachings,
of stoneface, rabbit-track, fox scat,
of peripheral flickerings, under
growth, gaps, goings on deep
in among thickets from where
eyes peer and branches creak

and out there or in here
a low note calls, it
calls and calls and calls

(Cae Carreg Corn is a field in Llanfaelog, Anglesey)

YOU'LL NEVER WALK ALONE
by Mike Tidswell

I love walking on Anglesey. Nothing too strenuous mind. It's funny how the first few miles feel really good and you ask yourself – why don't I do this more often? Then with at least three miles left, you remember the answer.

It is especially pleasant if you can walk with a friend, but somehow, for reasons I shall not share, I do most of my walking on my own.

At least I never have a disagreement, or get left behind. I always finish first. I have never yet got bored with my own company, nor have I run out of things to talk about. Besides, who knows who I may come across en route. On Anglesey there are all sorts of folks just waiting to pass a moment or two, to share a story, offer a glimpse into another world. It's like the song – You'll Never Walk Alone.

I had driven across the island to Moelfre. I left the car in the car park just short of the centre and walked back inland up a short hill towards the school. It must have been morning break. I stopped for a moment listening to the buzz of the children's voices. Oh to be young again – running around with hardly a care in the world, enjoying an age of hope and adventure, when the world is still exciting and seems to have been created for your own personal delight and pleasure.

But this was just the start of my adventure. I headed on across a couple of fields and then down by a small stream. It was so peaceful, if ever so slightly muddy!

More fields and then out onto a road. No traffic though. That's one of the things I love about Anglesey – the sun is shining, the sky is blue, the countryside is beautiful, it's a perfect day, and yet it seems as if there's only me here! Not a car in sight. It's all mine!

'Lligwy Burial Chamber' the old green sign declared. I went to investigate. Neolithic – about 5,000 years old! Between 15 and 30 people were buried there, placed under a vast rock weighing 25 tons! Who were they … these … Neoliths? How did they speak? How did they live, and how on earth did they lift that capstone into place?

I tried to imagine a people from before the time of Abraham, who lived here, walked these fields, worked and rested, cried and laughed in this very place. People who called it home. I focussed on the tomb. I tried to picture them, hear them even, but it was no use, no voices struggled to cross such a span of years. Nonetheless I had a powerful sense of being a visitor, almost an intruder, in a place that belonged to others that I could not quite reach.

A short distance down the road and there was something else. A sign for 'Din Lligwy'. I climbed a wall and walked towards a small tree covered hill carpeted in wild garlic. It was beautiful, enchanting. As I climbed the hill I felt as though I was journeying back in time to an age when these parts were covered with forests and those who lived here kept an unseen watch for strangers like me.

Nothing, though, could have prepared me for the sight that greeted me as I reached the top. It looked like a lost world. About half an acre enclosed within a stone boundary wall – five feet thick in places. There were at least two round houses and several rectangular buildings varying in size. Had I stumbled into the world of Arthur and Merlin? Was this where Anglesey folk lived at the time of the kings of Gwynedd? Was it even older than that?

Once again it was just me, no one else, just me, and this ancient village with its stone walls, full of voices from the past. If I could but open my ears and hear.

Din Lligwy was in fact built in the 4th century AD, a Romano-British settlement, a farm or villa, perhaps belonging to a local man who had prospered under the Roman occupation. Or maybe it was a remote haven of Britons who shared an uneasy relationship with the invaders. It was certainly a place of countless stories about life and death on the island of Môn long before the Normans arrived.

In one of the roundhouses there appeared to be a seat set into the wall facing the entrance – still there after 1700 years. I imagined myself invited into the stone walled home with its tall thatch roof, being made welcome and directed to that seat as if I were a special guest. I seemed to hear the laughter of children mixing with conversations of adults. In the distance, there was the faint sound of iron being worked in the large rectangular workshop. If I tried hard I could get just a glimpse of folk coming and going and doing what people do living together in a small community. For one short moment as I sat on that cold stone seat, Din Lligwy came alive.

All too soon though the images faded and the sounds melted back into the trees, leaving me with just a few stone walls.

I headed back, paying only very scant attention to the ruined 12th century chapel on my left. When your head has been wrestling with people who lived here in the 4th century, the medieval can wait for another time.

I could see the magnificent blue sea now. Ahead was Lligwy beach. I had last been there about 20 years ago when our two girls were quite young. We'd had a small inflatable boat and spent three wonderful days swimming, splashing about and building vast sandcastles. As I looked across the now almost empty expanse of sand I could see ramparts rising again and a moat being filled with buckets of water snatched from the sea. I watched Hannah and Eleanor playing. An image of sheer delight and happiness.

The route now followed the Coastal Path. There were cliffs and bays, birds and beaches. Oystercatchers were making a racket everywhere. And why not? You can even talk to them – when you've passed 60 and are on your own.

Dulas Bay. This place has a story to tell and no mistake. On 26 October 1859 the great steamship, *Royal Charter* came this way returning from Australia to Liverpool. There was a storm and it foundered on these very rocks. A staggering 459 people lost their lives that night. And these rocks saw it all.

No less a journalist than Charles Dickens was despatched from London to interview the few survivors and those who had watched helplessly from the shore. I suspect that they could not have found words to describe adequately the horror of that night.

I sat and looked out at the sea, thankful to be spared the cries of the perishing, perhaps because it was beyond my imagining. Even the oystercatchers seemed to respect my mood and left me to my reverie.

Of those who died, 140 were buried in Llanallgo churchyard. One of them was John Lewis of Bristol, the Purser. He was aged 54 and was a 'Kind and Devoted Husband' and was remembered by his 'Disconsolated Widow'. The air seemed full of 'disconsolation' that afternoon, but the waves continued to crash against the rocks of Dulas Bay, totally unmoved and uncaring. Here beauty was relentless and untamed.

Not far now from Moelfre. I paid my respects to Dic Evans, a former coxswain of the local lifeboat who once, in a storm, spent a full twelve hours at its wheel without respite. He now keeps permanent watch just around the corner from the harbour. I didn't think it right to distract him.

If you ever visit Moelfre you will find a delightful little harbour with an anchor by the roadside just across from the wonderful Ann's Pantry. You can go and have a word with old Dic – I'm sure he'd be delighted. But if you take the trouble to walk a little way inland and along the coast you may be fortunate enough to encounter a few of those who have, at one time or another, called this place home; people who once lived here, others who died here. There are many folk still with stories to share. Go by yourself or with a friend, but if you open your ears and open your heart to this island of ours – You'll Never Walk Alone.

ANOTHER FIGHT

by Cherry Bevan

Another fight, another war.
I ask 'What are they fighting for?'
This very young heroic band
Off in some Godforsaken land
That none of us had known before.

They each rely on one another
And treat each comrade as a brother
And think of this as only just
Another fight.

But when they come back home again
To this land of wind and rain
On looking back what will we find
In all those places left behind?
What will there be when we withdraw?
Another fight.

BETH YDI'R ATEB?

gan J Richard Williams

Fydd hi drosodd erbyn Dolig?
Fydd y lampau eto ynghyn?
Fydd 'na ymladd rhwng y gwledydd?
Fydd yr Hogia' 'nôl fan hyn?

Fydd 'na heddwch a thawelwch?
Fydd y byd yn ôl mewn trefn?
Fydda i yn filwr tybed?
Fydda i'n trin y tir drachefn?

Fydd 'na gerrig beddi newydd?
Fydd 'na gofio arwyr gwlad?
Fydd gwleidyddion wedi callio?
Fydd doluriau'n cael iachâd?

Bydd, fe fydd y byd mewn heddwch;
Fe fydd Fflam y Ffydd yn wyn.
Duw fydd eto yn teyrnasu
A'n byd yn lân, fel eira gwyn.

MEWN MYNWENT
I'R MILWYR A GOLLWYD
gan J Richard Williams

Nid oes un rhosyn ar eich carreg fedd
i darfu heddwch eich diderfyn hedd;
Dim ond tylluan a'i sgrechiadau prudd
a'r deigryn distaw sy'n dragwyddol olchi 'ngrudd.
Nid oes 'r un arwydd fod i'ch Mam na'ch Tad
alaru yma, gerllaw Maes y Gad;
Fe gawsoch air neu ddau mewn estron iaith
a'r dagrau'n ddistaw olchi 'ngruddiau llaith.

Ni ddaeth na châr na cheraint hoff ychwaith
i'ch hebrwng, ar eich unig, olaf daith;
Dim ond sŵn utgorn rwygodd aer y wawr
a'm dagrau llaith yn gwlitho llwch y llawr.
Ni ddaw'r un alwad eto i ryfela yn y drin
na chyfle i drin cleddyf llym ei fin;
Mae'r frwydr i chi, bellach, wedi troi
a holl elynion hedd sydd wedi ffoi.

Pwy ddaw a sefyll uwch y cerrig hyn?
Pwy ddaw a gosod yma flodyn gwyn?
Pan ddaw yr hiraeth fel rhyw saeth i'm bron
fe gofiaf i'r aruchel aberth hon.

LLAIS

gan Myfanwy Bennett Jones

Am ddau funud cysegredig
Nad oedd tarfu i fod arnynt,
Safem yn dorf, yn llenwi'r stryd,
Cerbydau'n llonydd o ddeutu:
Rhai ohonom o deuluoedd a fylchwyd,
Rhai ag atgof o gyfeillion y profwyd yr hunllef o'u colli,
Rhai ym malchder sglein medalau;
Ac, wrth gwrs, 'roedd rhai yn stond mewn lifrau,
A'r gwaethaf, o bosib', o'u blaenau.
Pawb ohonom
Mewn tristwch atgofus,
Mewn gweddi am i heddwch ymledu,
Am i Dywysog Tangnefedd gael ei le.

Ac yna, uwch ein pennau,
Fe chwarddodd brân.

LLYN CERRIG BACH

by Ross Davies

I was brought up on Anglesey and went to school in Beaumaris then I entered college in Bangor in 1946. As I was a student of ancient history, I was allowed into Bangor's tiny museum in College Road and allowed to draw and record archaeological finds, even to handle them. All the Llyn Cerrig Bach artefacts had been transferred there and the experience of handling such precious things, crafted by man over a thousand years ago, was one that I have never forgotten. I'd like to tell you more about the story of these artefacts and where they were found.

Llyn Cerrig Bach could be loosely translated as 'the lake of small stones'. A strange name you might think for a lake or a pool, but it was probably quite shallow and lying in flat, marshy ground, in the west of Anglesey. Whatever the reason, Llyn Cerrig Bach held a secret that had been hidden from view for over a thousand years.

It was during the Second World War years, *circa* 1943, that this secret came to light at the RAF airfield at Valley. Britain had struck an agreement for a lease-land scheme with America, for major armaments such as planes and tanks. Delivery of these, across the Atlantic in wartime, needed places of convenience and safety. RAF Valley was chosen as one such place.

However, because of the size of the American bombers, the

Valley airstrip proved to be inadequate for landing and takeoff. It was decided to extend and widen the strip into the marshy ground ahead which included the shallow lake called Llyn Cerrig Bach. As men and machinery were in short supply during the war, local farmers had to be employed to clear the area using their small Ferguson tractors. It was during this work that one of the tractors became bogged down in thick mud and the farmer had to call on another tractor driver to haul him out.

Whilst searching for a rope to tie the two vehicles together, he spotted a piece of metal poking out of the mud. On tugging it out, it proved to be a length of metal chain long enough for the purpose. The tractor was successfully towed out and the chain thrown to one side.

By now, an archaeological group from Bangor had arrived on the scene hoping that something of interest might have had been unearthed. They knew that the whole island was steeped in history, but the finds at Llyn Cerrig Bach proved to be breath-taking.

The linked chain, so carelessly thrown aside, was identified as a slave chain for prisoners. It had interlinked metal neck collars and was so well crafted that the passage of centuries had not affected its strength. It was well over a thousand years old. Further finds revealed nearly one hundred other artefacts, including weapons and equipment connected with war and horsemanship. There was a chariot wheel, chariot furniture and fittings; also, cauldrons, beakers and fragments of decorated bronze in the distinctive *La Tene* design.

La Tene is pattern and symbol rather than pictorial or naturalistic.

It originated in Switzerland and as the Celts moved across Europe, it appeared in Ireland, south-east England, Yorkshire and finally, Anglesey.

All the finds were dated between 150 BC and 50 AD. They were thought to be sacramental offerings made by Druid priests into the lake. Anglesey must have been an important centre of Druidic religion for the whole of Britain at that time. After the Roman invasion of 61 AD the Druid faith slowly died out.

TOY BOY
by Olive Blundell

I wish you'd be my toy-boy
And come and live with me.
I'd make you very welcome.
You could even have a key.

I like men that are tall and dark
And handsome, too (if poss.)
You'd take me out to all the shows
But I'd still be the boss!

Each night we'd go out dancing.
We'd travel far and wide.
I'd never be alone again
With you there at my side.

I'd show you off to all my friends,
How they would envy me.
You see, I'm in my seventies
And you're just thirty-three!

But, even the best of things must end.
My money's running out
And when it's gone, you'd go as well.
I know, without a doubt.

Then I'll go back to wishing,
Dreaming my time away.
But – maybe if I win the pools –
You might come back one day.

THE WALK
by E Pritchard

Sally came downstairs feeling woolly-headed after having slept late. She arrived in the kitchen just as her son, Philip, was stuffing his packed lunch into his bag in readiness to spend the day fishing with his friend. 'Hi Mum, 'bye Mum!' he said with a smile, coming over to kiss her cheek.

'Why didn't you wake me? Has Sian already gone to work?' she said stifling a yawn before her gaze took in the state of the kitchen. 'Oh, for goodness' sake, look at the mess in here!'

'Yes, she slept late too and had to dash off and I've got to go too. Tom's Dad is picking me up now.' They both heard the toot of a car horn.

'Have a good time. I'll just carry on slaving away as usual while my children do what they want.' She knew she sounded bitter.

Phil came over and gave her a hug. 'Aw Mum, don't be like that. It's a beautiful day and one day your prince will come!' Off he dashed and the door slammed, leaving Sally feeling guilty and miserable for having snapped at her sunny natured son. She knew she was lucky to have two wonderful children, a daughter of 18 and a son of 15, who were no trouble at all even though they were teenagers. She was proud of them and felt she must have done something right as she had brought them up single-handedly since their father left when Phil was a baby.

She sighed deeply and sat down. Meg, the Border collie, came up to her and put her head on her knee. Ruffling the dog's fur she suddenly decided. 'Why don't we go for a walk?' Meg didn't need asking twice and, claws scrabbling on the tiled floor, she dashed to wait at the back door. Sally clipped on the lead and, with a last glance at the messy kitchen, she picked up her mobile phone and locked the door behind her.

It really was a beautiful day and Sally decided to head towards Porthdafarch. Before she was even half way there she felt her spirits lift as she filled her lungs with the scent of the countryside. The sky was blue and the sun was warm. There were clumps of primroses in the hedgerows and violets and celandines. Striding along, she soon came to the beach. The tide was out and the waves gleamed in the sunlight. Unclipping Meg's lead she headed for the cliff path. Meg bounded ahead and came back with a stick which she dropped at Sally's feet. Unable to resist the pleading brown eyes as they looked alternately down at the stick and up into her face, she played the game as they walked along. After a while she stopped to get her breath and gazed out to sea. She felt rejuvenated and resolved to make a special meal for them all that evening. Sian hadn't said she was going out and Phil would be hungry after a day's fishing. She turned and there was Meg sitting waiting for her but this time she had a huge stick in her mouth. 'Where on earth did you get that, you daft dog, that isn't the one I've been throwing!' she laughed. Suddenly Meg heard something and saw a young rabbit scurrying away. She turned to run after it and the stick caught Sally behind her knees. She slithered down the grassy slope at the top of the cliff, her hands trying in vain to grasp hold of the grass or anything to halt her slide. Horror. Panic. No time even to cry out before she reached an over-hanging rock and then fell heavily down the cliff. Her body landed with a thud. She lay there crumpled and still. Mean-while, Meg was in a state of confusion at the top of the cliff. After unsuccessfully chasing the rabbit she came running back to where she had left Sally and was puzzled when there was no sign of her. She was scurrying back and forth and barking anxiously. A couple walked past and stopped with her. 'Do you think she's lost?' asked the girl.

'No, she's probably from the farm over there and has chased a rabbit or something,' said her companion. 'She'll find her way home.' And they went on their way.

It was several hours later when Sally started coming to her senses. Her lips were dry and she couldn't breathe deeply so guessed she had cracked or broken some ribs. The pain in her leg, ankle and hip made her think there was something broken there too. She knew that she desperately needed help. The pain as she moved to try and get her mobile out of her pocket made her cry out and, to her dismay, she found the phone had been broken in her fall. Drifting in and out of consciousness, she was aware that her predicament was serious. She was hidden from the path by the overhanging rock face above her. She was shivering now and, to her horror, she realised that the tide was coming in. She couldn't take a deep enough breath to shout for help because of the pain in her ribs but, she asked herself, who would hear her anyway? She tried to shuffle herself away from the incoming tide but her agony made it futile. She lay there making all sorts of bargains with God. She started to cry as she thought of her children; her beautiful, wonderful children. They didn't deserve to be left alone to cope with life. She was annoyed that she hadn't been up in time to see Sian before she went to work and sad that she had been so grumpy with Phil. She remembered that the last words he said to her were 'One day your prince will come.' Fat chance of that now. The incoming tide had reached her feet now, not breaking waves but gentle, insistent ones.

Suddenly she heard a terrific clatter as a helicopter came close. It turned and hovered above her – big, noisy and yellow. It had seen her! The winchman was already on his way down to her. 'Thank you, God,' she smiled and as she looked up at the helicopter she knew that whoever was piloting it, her Prince had come.

LADY IN THE LANE
by Geoffrey Lincoln

First I saw you one bright night,
The moon was shining, stars were bright,
Wandering there beneath the trees,
Hair stirred by a phantom breeze.

Just a whisper in the air,
Then I knew that you were there.
Were you real or was my mind
Seeking what it couldn't find?

What sadness hid behind those eyes
Shadowed in a faint disguise?
What tragedies, what passions spent
That made your shoulders sadly bent?

Several times I watched you pass,
No indentation in the grass.
We never spoke, we didn't stare,
And yet you knew that I was there.

And now you've gone, I search the night
For that soft whisper and the sight
Beneath the blazing stars of you;
There's nothing else that I can do.

Lonely lady in the lane,
Will we ever meet again?
How I long to see you there,
The glint of moonlight in your hair.

MYND
gan Morfudd Owen (16 oed)

Paid â mynd.
Fy ngadael i.
Ddim fel hyn.

Arhosa.
Ddim am byth.
Ond ddim eto.
Dwi'm yn barod.

Fedrai ddim dy golli di,
Felly paid â gadael.
Beth wna i hebddot ti?
Fy rheswm yn diflannu.

Nid dy ddewis di,
Dwi'n dallt.
Ond tria, plîs.
Tria aros efo fi.

Mi wna i unrhywbeth
I'th gael di i aros efo fi.
Bydd cyn gryfed â fi,
A chwffia i aros.

Wyt ti eisio mynd?
Dy ddewis di ydi gadael?
Newidia dy feddwl.
Arhosa fymryn mwy.

Mi fydd y byd yn unig,
Yn brifo,
Yn dy golli di.

Oeda.
Ti'm isio bod yn seren uwchben.
Wastad yno, yn edrych.
Mae gen ti ddawns ar ôl.
Cân i'w chanu.
Soned i'w sgwennu.

Un ffafr ofynna i: aros.
Sefa, eistedda, dim ots be wnei di,
Ond cadw'n glir o'r drws yna.

Paid â mynd.
Efo fi, ti'n saff.
Efo chdi, dwi'n fyw.

THE SILENT CRYING
by Eleanor Spratt

The estate agent greets us in the front grounds which are large, overgrown and neglected but it is the house that immediately draws my attention. I gaze at it in amazement. It is beautifully proportioned and part of the façade is in the gothic style. Black frames starkly outline the windows against the fading cream washed exterior. Yet ... there is something rather sinister about its appearance.

It is early March and a cold, bright morning. The house, like the surrounding trees, reflects the late winter season and stands silent and without adornment. I wonder if the warmer days of springtime and summer can bring it back to life.

Entering the cold porch, I feel a shiver down my spine. However, the sun streams warmly into the large reception rooms which are on either side of the main hall and fills them with light. Floor to ceiling sash windows frame the Snowdonia mountains and I catch my breath. Awesome! We discuss the place with enthusiasm and our words echo around the emptiness of the rooms and bounce back from the high ceiling.

At the back of the house, it is dark and very cold.

'You can see that the place needs modernising,' says the agent. 'There's no central heating and it's a very old fashioned kitchen.'

'Who on earth has been living here in these conditions?' I ask.

'I really don't know. It's been empty for almost two years and was rented out before that. I do know that if you make a reasonable offer the owners will be happy to consider it. But let me show you the upstairs.'

I love the wide central staircase that rises elegantly to the first floor and then narrows for the final leg to the top floor under the eaves. At one time this must have been the home of a gentleman farmer and the servants would have lived up here. This silent house would have buzzed with life – the maids up early, setting and lighting the fires and the cook busy in the kitchen.

'There's plenty of space for an en-suite in this big bedroom.' The agent's voice brings me back to earth. I'm sure it would be possible to return this house to its former glory.

'What do you think?' whispers my husband.

'It could be made into a wonderful home,'' I reply, 'but somehow, something isn't quite right.' The chill I feel in the house seems to penetrate further and deeper than just into the stones and mortar. I shiver involuntarily.

'It would be different once heating is installed,' he says. 'But is it too large for us?'

'Being practical – yes, but the views are spectacular and the house is very grand. It's what we've always wanted. Let's go and have a look around the grounds.'

Outside, we wander around the dilapidated outbuildings that would once have stored hay and crops, and stabled the working horses.

'It would be a major project,' my husband sighs. 'We'll have to consider it very carefully.'

I can't stop thinking about the house so a few weeks later I return on my own to have a second look. The 'For Sale' sign is still there. The hedges are now thick and leafy, and I park my car in the lay-by near the wrought-iron gate. Checking that there is no one about, I stealthily lift the latch and walk into the grounds. It seems as if the house is staring at me. 'Tell me your secret,' I ask.

Suddenly I feel strange and detached as if the physical boundaries around me have slipped away. I sit on a low, stone wall to steady myself and it is as if I have lost all sense of time. It is then that I hear the sound of a baby crying.

The sun rises behind the mountains and slowly spreads its warm glow upon the summer-seared leaves of the trees. The hay has been cut and stands in small haycocks in the fields. The heavy horses stir and whinny softly to one another in the stables. The farm hands prepare the feed. Evan Roberts measures out the oats but he has his mind on other matters.

How can Martha be so sure that I am the father of her child? She has probably lain with other men. She wants to tie me down but she's picked the wrong man. I don't have the money to support a wife and family. I can't bear to look at the child. She'll regret the words she shouted at me last night.

He finishes his work quickly, looks furtively around and then slips away by the side of the beautiful new stately house that stands in front of the farm buildings. He disappears through a gap in the hedge.

A few hours later he returns clutching a bundle under his arm. He has used local tracks and ditches to keep well out of sight. However, an old woman is looking out of her window and wonders what he is doing. She is the last person in the locality to see him before his humiliating return.

Meanwhile, Martha still feels upset and aggrieved by Evan's treatment of her the previous night. Her face blushes as she recalls his unkind accusation.

Of course the dear baby is his and it's only right that he should take responsibility. How dare he say that she went with other men. Thank goodness she still had work on the small farm near the village, otherwise how could she manage?

She leaves her child sleeping in the cradle and goes into the shed to begin her work. The cows are waiting in the milking parlour. Their udders hang heavy and full. The buttons on the grey bodice of her coarse cotton dress begin to pull apart as the time draws near for her to feed her own child. She completes her task and hastens back.

On her return she finds an empty cradle. Her anguished screams can be heard throughout the village.

Several days pass before the baby is found. Its tiny, cold body is wrapped tightly in its woollen shawl and it lies beneath some straw in a corner of one of the sheds where Evan Roberts had been working. He is the chief suspect. Someone saw him clambering aboard the Straits ferry at Foel on the day of the child's disappearance and he has not been seen since.

Some weeks later there is a tip-off that Roberts is working in Flint. He is apprehended, arrested and escorted back to Anglesey to stand trial. He is in poor shape when he gets off the boat. His handsome face looks haggard and dark patches surround his eyes which remain focused on the ground.

The trial is to take place at the court in Beaumaris on the 20th October 1824. The punishment for murder is execution by hanging. Evan's family are shocked at the thought of the death sentence. He claims he is innocent. He says he left Anglesey so that he could get away from Martha and the child. He wanted to make a new life for himself.

The jury listens to all the evidence. It seems a straightforward case to those spectators in the courthouse. They believe that Evan Roberts is guilty, without a doubt. It's a 'cut and dried case' if ever there was one. The court falls silent as the jurymen return to give their verdict – 'Not guilty.'

It is based on the grounds that they are not satisfied as to the identity of the baby's body. Evan Roberts is acquitted.

Martha trembles when she hears the verdict. She covers her pale face with her hands and weeps. Local people mutter among themselves that the family must have bribed the jury.

A sudden loud whirring sound in the sky startles me out of my daydreaming. A yellow search and rescue helicopter is above me – someone is in trouble on the mountains. My gaze returns to the house and I know that I have the answer to my question. I gather a posy of wild flowers and lay it on the doorstep in memory of Martha and her baby.

References:
Crime and Punishment at Beaumaris *by Margaret Hughes.*

ENERGY FLOWS FOR MÔN
by Chris Pritchard

An island bathed by chilly seas,
subjected to a tidal flow.
Its shores washed by the creamy foam
and governed by the moon's soft glow.

Its earthworks secretive within,
withholding mineral treasures rare,
beneath the rolling swells of Môn,
prizes, for such men who dare.

A westerly windswept land,
where turbines march in ordered row
to capture that elusive force,
of power, where the harsh winds blow.

A bastion of technology
rears up upon the northern shore.
A flash of nuclear fission bright,
a power that humans should deplore?

Our lust for power in all its forms,
should not deface our lovely isle.
Be careful with this precious source
and temper greed with need awhile.

A MOST HEART-RENDING CALAMITY
by Mike Tidswell

LLANIDAN CHURCH, BRYNSIENCYN, FEBRUARY 2012

'We sing the hymn – Eternal Father, strong to save…' The small congregation rises.

'O hear us when we cry to Thee, for those in peril on the sea.'

'We have come here today,' announced the vicar, 'to give thanks for this man, given back to us, unknown and yet loved as a part of our community. We join in a celebration of his life and the life of the others who died with him nearly 200 years ago. They were deeply mourned and sadly missed. Their loss devastated the people of this place. Many years later we meet to commit him, to offer up the names of the others and to leave them all to rest in the arms of our Eternal Father.'

NORTH WALES POLICE HEADUARTERS, COLWYN BAY (JANUARY 2012)

He was male, 5 foot 9, aged between 40 and 50. His remains are a little battered, which is entirely consistent with having been in the sea some time before being washed up on Llanddwyn Island and then eventually covered by sand.

There is a small hairline fracture to the right of the skull that shows no sign of healing and is consistent with a blow to the head at about the time of death. I can't be precise as to whether it was just before or just afterwards. It is, however, quite small and unlikely to have been the cause of death although it would not have helped him in his struggle. There are no other significant wounds and I think we can be pretty sure that he died from drowning – a long time ago. It's difficult to say from the actual remains just how long, but there were a few coins found directly underneath him. All George III and dated between 1805 and 1819. Assuming that they were his, he could have died no earlier than 1819 and probably no later than 1840 or so – which feels about right.

FROM THE WITNESS STATEMENT – HUGH WILLIAMS (AUGUST 1820)
Everyone on a sinking boat reacts differently. One man just clung to the side and started to cry, others tried to throw stuff we were taking to the market over the side and some began to bale the water. But it wasn't much use, if all happened so quickly.

We might have panicked, but there wasn't time.

It didn't seem real. We'd all made the crossing dozens of times before – it was just a bit of a swell, a bit of a blow, we'd been through the like before and we'd do it again.

Everyone knew about the currents. Quite tricky the Straits if you don't know your way around. But the wind, none of us expected that. It came from nowhere.

Truth is, it had been travelling for hours across the ocean and now it chose to funnel between the mountains and the island, picking up speed as it did. It was high tide and that is when the currents flow wildly in both directions at the same time. The wind just whipped that lot up into a manic maelstrom.

The ferryman seemed to know what he was doing, which was comforting, but the boat was severely overloaded, which wasn't.

We were in trouble as soon as the squall hit us. A rope tangled around the top of the sail and made it almost impossible to handle. Someone tried to climb the mast to free it but fell into the water. When we attempted to reach him, the boat started to capsize and then it just fell apart. One minute we were baling and the next, everyone was in the sea fighting for their lives.

Oh Saviour, whose almighty word, the winds and waves submissive heard ... Oh hear us when we cry to Thee for those in peril on the sea.

THE LAST MEMORY OF ROBERT THOMAS, MILLER, BODOWYR (5 AUGUST 1820)

A flash of light filled my head as it struck a rock on the seabed. Then, for a moment, darkness, before the thrashing of others brought me quickly back. I was dimly aware of arms and legs fighting for survival; of the heavy pieces of the boat descending at speed around me; of the pounding of my pulse; of the pain in my chest and of the need to get to the surface.

The current kept dragging me, flipping me and turning me. I didn't even know which was up. I must have surfaced because I opened my mouth to breathe but it filled with water. I started to cough, but only succeeded in gulping even more of the sea into my aching lungs.

Where was Eleanor – my wife? I had to save her, but I couldn't see her. I could see nothing in the swirling muddy water. Then incredibly, for a moment in all this madness, I thought I could see the children: John, Robert, Jane, Thomas and the others, back at the mill at Bodowyr. As clear as crystal they were, all smiling at me and beckoning me. But just as suddenly, they were gone and I was left wrestling with the sea.

I saw the sky. At last I could breathe. There was hope, but I still had no sense of direction, Then, bang! Another wave and I was under again.

My lungs were squeezed even smaller, my ears were pounding, my heart was beating like a great military drum and all above was the rumble of the swirling water, but then somehow I was heading up. I broke the surface just in time. I choked. Water flowed through my nose, my throat burned and my head was shrieking. I opened my mouth to shout but all that I managed was a spew of bubbles.

I had little time left. I had to keep fighting. But I was incredibly tired, I could barely see. Every part of me ached. My strength was all but gone. My lungs were about to burst and pain hammered through my head – enough to make my eyes pop.

Just as I knew I could take no more a voice inside my aching head whispered

O Sacred Spirit, who didst brood upon the chaos dark and rude, Who bade's its angry tumult cease and gavest light and life and peace. O hear us when we cry to Thee for those in peril on the sea.

Cold numbing claws began to pull me closer, to squeeze out what little I had left.

I screamed a silent scream, 'Eleanor, I'm sorry!' My arms and legs began to spasm frantically and then, only darkness. Darkness above me, darkness below me, darkness in my head. Total darkness, still and black and complete.

FROM *THE HISTORY OF ANGLESEY SHIPWRECKS*
On 5 August 1820 a ferry with 23 passengers left Llanidan bound for Caernarfon. Midway across the Menai Straits it was hit by a fierce squall and sank. All but one of those on board, Hugh Williams, were drowned.

FROM THE *NORTH WALES GAZETTE*, THURSDAY (AUGUST 10 1820)
On Saturday last, being market day at Carnarvon, when the farmer and their domestics from Anglesey were crossing the river in great numbers a most heart-rending calamity occurred, at a ferry recently established from Llanidan across to Plas Bruton, in about a mile of Carnarvon. The boat started with about 23 passengers besides a variety of articles intended for Carnarvon market.

They had not proceeded quite half way over, it flowing fresh when the boatman, having climbed up the small mast to disentangle a rope attached to the sail, unfortunately fell into the water. In the rush to save him the pressure proved too great for the crazy bark to sustain; and in a moment it separated nearly in the centre. Dreadful to relate, with the exception of one individual, the whole were engulfed in the waves. Their screams were heard for an instant resounding to the shore, but in the returning wave they were forever hushed.

LLANIDAN CHURCH, BRYNSIENCYN (FEBRUARY 2012)

'And so Heavenly Father we thank you that after 200 years you have given us back our brother who we now commit to you. We pray for all those who died in that heart-rending calamity and for all who mourned.

We thank you for the love of those who cared for the bereaved and bereft, for the courage, determination and inspiration, of those who, despite their loss, continued to be your people.

We join with them in praying that all who perished or suffered loss, may rest in the peace of your eternal arms and that we may learn from the example of their faith and fortitude.

Amen'

And ever let there rise to Thee, glad hymns of praise from land and sea.

ANGLESEY, FEBRUARY

by Geoffrey Lincoln

No golden dawn today,
but feel the merry wind,
soft from the west, as it scatters
grey clouds across the Straits,
revealing a fleeting radiance
beyond the distant heights.

See the shore
washed clean by the ebb tide,
reflecting the wet sand;
the wheeling gulls
celebrating the arrival
of another morning.

And now, through the rain,
the sun appears,
beckoning a rainbow
over the sombre landscape,
its brightness rising
from the forest's murmur.

Listen to the curlew's call
stirring the quietness,
while homeward lapwings
glitter joyfully across
the broken sky, cascading
to the lake's margin.

As the short day closes,
stand by me at the window
and watch the moon rise
behind the bare branches
proclaiming the arrival
of a frosty night.

Within the twinkle
of that distant star
is an eternity of music –
and our dancing never ends.

DYN YSWIRIANT

gan Alan Wyn Roberts

Rhag llif a chryndod daear
Bu'i bolisïau'n ddengar;
Ond methodd iddo'i hun yn lân
Rhag tân i drefnu cyfar.

THE GIFT
by Joy Mawby

Mr Bagaj trudged slowly along the drab High Street in the winter rain.

'I'm old and tired,' he thought. 'No good to myself and a burden to Ela and Dafydd. I should never have left my own country. At least I had friends there. What's the use of going on?'

So deep was he in his despair that he didn't notice the lorry.

Suddenly something fell out of the dismal watery sky. Kerphlat! It fell at Mr Bagaj's feet. It was a dirty beige and streaked with filth. It throbbed and twitched and tried to move forward. Startled, he bent to look. He saw a body, two stick legs, claws, a scraggy neck and a head with black bead eyes staring back at him.

Mr Bagaj had lived on a farm for most of his life but even he had difficulty in identifying this almost bald thing, this skin and bone, as a chicken. It struggled upright and made a sudden dart on to the road in front of an oncoming car. Without thinking, Mr Bagaj dived after it, ignoring the car's horn and the shouts of the driver. He caught the bird and pulled it back just in time. He pushed it inside his anorak and looked round, trying to fathom where it had come from. A lorry had stopped at the traffic lights. Mr Bagaj squinted at it and saw words he didn't understand. Under the writing there was a picture of a fat hen next to one of a big pie.

231

His eyes widened as he realised that the chicken had somehow flapped from its prison inside a lorry which had been on its way to some sort of chicken factory. He made an instant decision. 'I, Bagaj, found this hen. I've saved it from death. It is mine. I will make soup with it. It will be supper for Ela, Dafydd and me. For once I have something to give.'

The hen was reviving in the warmth of his jacket. It was making little clucking noises and moving its head softly against Mr Bagaj's chest. Cradling it gently, he hurried back to the cottage where he lived with his daughter and son in law. He went into the small kitchen. He had dealt with many chickens. This one was weak and would be easily despatched. In spite of being so thin, it would make good Ukrainian soup. His mouth watered at the thought. Now the hen made no sound but looked up at him, its sharp eyes alert.

And then he knew he couldn't do it. He couldn't kill this creature which looked at him with such trust in her eyes. 'I, Bagaj found you, just as you found me,' he said 'You escaped and I saved you twice from death. You deserve to live.'

He put some water in a saucer and gave her a few crumbs from the loaf in the fridge.

'Clara', he told her. 'I shall call you Clara. Tomorrow I shall buy you some corn to eat and see about a proper home for you but now I find somewhere for you to be safe and warm.' He went outside, closing the kitchen door carefully. He found the red recycling box in the outhouse and emptied most of its contents into a black plastic sack. He left some newspaper at the bottom. 'This will do for now,' he told Clara, lifting her in and placing the box in front of the boiler. He watched as she fidgeted, settled and finally tucked her head under her wing. Then he too fell asleep in the armchair next to her.

'What on earth is this?' Mr Bagaj was woken by Ela's voice. He opened his eyes to see her and Dafydd bending over Clara.

'She Clara, my hen,' he said and then he explained what had happened. They were both laughing by the time he'd finished.

'You old softie,' Dafydd said.

'You can't keep her in here, though, Papa.' There was an edge of anxiety to Ela's voice.

'No, no. Can I have little garden? I build shelter for her, and run, please?'

'Of course you can,' said Dafydd, grateful that his father in law at last seemed interested in something. 'Come and I'll show you where you can make Clara's house. That wild bit on the right, I think.' He looked at Ela and she nodded, eyes shining. 'And,' Dafydd continued as they went out, 'I think my Dad has got some odd wood and bits of wire you could have. We can pop round and see him after tea. There's something we want to tell you both.

That night, lying in bed, Mr Bagaj felt flooded with happiness. How he'd hated the fact that his only child, his beloved Ela had decided to marry a Welshman and settle on an island called Ynys Môn so far away from the Ukraine. She had only meant to stay here for six months.

'I want to go Papa,' she'd said. 'Masha went last year. She's got friends there. She says there's plenty of work in the summer. It'll be such an experience for me.'

And now look at her, blossoming into motherhood.

'And look at me, Bagaj,' he thought, 'living in a foreign land where I've just discovered that I'm going to be a grandfather. On top of all this, Dafydd's father has enough wood and wire to build Clara a fine home.' Mr Bagaj was smiling when he fell asleep.

It is summer. Mr Bagaj and Clara sit side by side on cushioned chairs, in the small back garden. They are enjoying the sunshine. Mr Bagaj surveys the scene before him. Roses bloom all round Clara's house – and a fine house it is. It has red painted walls, thatched roof and lattice windows. Inside is a cosy roosting room, access by sliding hatch. There is a run in front which leads into the little garden. Nearby is a shiny blue pram. Clara is preening her glossy russet feathers. From time to time, head on one side, she regards the old man whose voice she knows so well. Through half closed eyes, Mr Bagaj looks at Clara whose ecstasy at seeing him each morning fills him with joy.

'You three look comfortable. Any room for me?' Looking over the fence is Dafydd's father, Huw Tomos.

'Come in, Huw, come in. Ela make lemonade this morning. She gone post office but you come, have lemonade.'

Mr Bagaj fetches another chair and as he goes in for the lemonade, he remembers the first time he had a proper conversation with Huw. It was over a year ago. The day after he'd found Clara, Hugh invited him round for a cup of coffee. A pile of wood and chicken wire was standing by the gate ready for Dafydd to collect later. Then, with the little English Mr Bagaj had learned, helped by sign language and a Ukrainian dictionary, the two men discovered that they had much in common. Both were widowers, both had been farmers and had a keen interest in wildlife and the countryside. Their strongest bond, of course, was their love for Ela and Dafydd and their excitement over the expected grandchild. As Mr Bagaj was leaving, Huw had asked, with accompanying appropriate actions, 'Will your hen lay eggs, do you think?'

'No. No eggs but she be friend for me.'

Huw had almost offended Mr Bagaj by laughing, but seeing his straight face, quickly assumed a serious expression himself and said, 'Good idea.' And he'd patted Mr Bagaj on the shoulder.

The two men built Clara's house together and later Huw took Mr Bagaj to many beautiful places on the island. A deep friend-ship had developed and next year they are planning to visit the Ukraine together.

When Mr Bagaj returns with the lemonade Huw is bending over the pram, making baby noises to their granddaughter, Eleri Mai. They stand side by side in joint adoration of their pink-cheeked, dimpled darling. They are roused by a raucous squawking. Clara's chair is empty.

'Where Clara? She gone.' Alarmed, Mr Bagaj gives Huw the lemonade and makes for the run. 'What wrong Clara? Where are you?' Clara flutters from the roosting room, voice still strident. She struts on to the grass and pecks at the flower border, giving her master one of her sideways glances. He peers into the hen-scented gloom of the chicken house and gives a gasp. He reaches in and then turns a radiant face to Huw. On his outstretched hand lies something small, brown and oval.

'Look,' he breathes, 'It warm egg. It perfect gift from Clara for Eleri Mai.'

ON RETURNING TO SEA
by Neil Brooks

After all those years ashore, Sir,
I fell for the five card trick.
All those soft years ashore, Sir,
A-swinging round the pick.
I thought I'd get away, Sir,
To the harder life once more,
To the merry, boozing life, Sir,
'Stead Holyhead's life ashore.

But ...

Life's not what it was at all, Sir,
When I was a lad at sea,
When even the boys were men, Sir,
Drinking creosote 'stead of tea.
Life's much too soft aboard, Sir
Why, I remember when
You were lucky if you ate, Sir,
Not this 'What? Steak again?'
When Mates knew where they was, Sir,
By plotting on their chart;
Radar wasn't heard of,
Navigation was an art.

And women brought bad luck, Sir,
If you took 'em out of port.
Well, maybe in them days, Sir,
They was a different sort.

Now 'lectronics have us beat, Sir,
Though I must admit they're good.
Give me marlin spikes for fingers.
And Stockholm Tar for blood
I guess those men have gone, Sir,
And it makes me kind of sad,
But them far off bloody days, Sir,
In truth, that was so bad!

TO LOVE, HONOUR AND OBEY
By KMM

Look Max, the tide is out and there's a lovely stretch of sand where you can have a good run and practise your obedience training.

What are you waiting for? Off you go.

Oh, I see, you want your ball. Here it is on the back seat, the bright orange one on a rope that you chose in the pet shop. Well, 'chose' is probably not the right word. It's the one you walked out with and I had to go back and pay for.

You don't want that one? It's got to be the rotten, old, chewed up tennis ball? Right, if that's the one you want. Here we go – FETCH!

No, I haven't got it. I threw it over there. Go and fetch it.

I said 'fetch'. That means you not me.

All right, just this once…

Here you are, now don't take the ball into the water. I said not-in-the-water. Not in the…

If you think I'm wading out there to get your ball, think again. And it's no use standing there barking, I am not going into the water. I am absolutely, definitely not going in the sea…

Now look what you've made me do! I've got a boot full of seawater, my jeans are soaking – and here's your ball. That's it. We're going home. Now!

What do you mean you're not getting into the car without your ball? I haven't got it. You were carrying it. Ah, I see, it's rolled right under that car over there.

Stay there! Stay!

I can't reach it and I am not getting down on my hands and knees under someone else's car just to get your rotten, old tennis ball. Leave it where it is, you've got plenty more at home.

I said – leave!

If you want to stay and guard it all night that's your choice but stop barking, people are staring.

No. I am not crawling under that car…

Excuse me? Uh no, I am not trying to get myself run-over, unless the owner drives away and doesn't notice me…

It's your car? Oh, I can explain everything. You see, I was retrieving my dog's ball.

No, he's not a retriever. He's a collie and he won't go home until he's got his ball back. You know what dogs are like.

You don't? Well, they're just like children really.

You haven't got any of those either. Very sensible.

Well, I'll be getting home now I've got the ball. That's my car over there, the one with the black and white … Max? MAX! MAAAAAX …"

ANGLESEY, BELOVED

by the late Jacqueline Vaucouleur

Yet once again I rejoice to hear
    In the pattering rain from the hill
The voice of Anglesey, soft and clear,
    A loving welcome for me still.

The rain has called, and the wind has called
    The compelling sea, the sky, the stone;
From the far-off North I have heard the call
    Where I slept, aloof and alone.

I answered the call, and come to bend
    My head low to the wind and the rain
To be purged, and to find in the end,
    A refuge from sorrow and pain.

But pain is here for me, too, I know,
    Pangs wrought by sunshine, wavelet and cloud;
Here, where the sweet winds of Heaven blow,
    And the Harp of God sings aloud.

Anglesey, love of my life and soul;
    Each tender love of my life in part
And all my deep love of Life in whole,
    Môn Mam Cymru – home of my heart.

REMEMBERING ANGLESEY
by Rosalind Pulvertaft

I loved you, Anglesey,
Your grey bones thrusting through
Grey rocks that crown your wind-scoured fields
Where hawthorns crouch contorted.
Your lanes lined green with Alexanders,
A froth of fairy blackthorn,
Whole hillsides aglow with golden gorse
And everywhere pink campion.

Anglesey, island of energy.
White giants striding across your hills,
Knife-blades that slice your endless winds
And thrust round their silent thrumming.
Pebbles of Cemlyn, veined and polished
Moulded by sucking seas.
Bright seas that surge around your rocks
And stretch across to Erin.

But I feared you Anglesey.
I feared your brooding nuclear power.
Power that huddles squat on Wylfa head
Spreading its desolation.
I feared the sad and sightless houses,

Cherished gardens, wild, abandoned,
Desolation creeping to Cemaes
Blackmailed with money.

I remember Cemaes where tourists stay
Seeking to make a home.
Sadly now they seek
Their lights, their shops, their bustling crowds.
Here are only seagulls screaming
Along the beach the cold waves breaking,
Sun and sand a distant longing
A moment in the long year.

I was saddened, Anglesey,
By your dying towns.
Shopkeepers bravely clinging on,
Holding out against the rising tide
Of supermarket and internet.
Villages that have lost their heart,
Houses turning their backs upon the streets
No school, no shops, no pubs.

I left you, Anglesey
But I remember still your sun and wind,
Settled as I am in Southern valleys.
I will not forget
The words of Welsh you taught me
Or the friends who still abide on Ynys Môn
That bright island, leaping upwards
Through surrounding waves.

INDEX OF WRITERS

247